ARDUINO FOR ARTISTS

HOW TO CREATE STUNNING MULTIMEDIA ART WITH ELECTRONICS

ARDUINO FOR ARTISTS

HOW TO CREATE STUNNING MULTIMEDIA ART WITH ELECTRONICS

BY MATTHEW McCLAIN

NEW DEGREE PRESS
ARDUINO FOR ARTISTS
How to Create Stunning Multimedia Art with Electronics

ISBN   978-1-63676-854-0   *Paperback*
           978-1-63730-188-3   *Kindle Ebook*
           978-1-63730-298-9   *Ebook*

For My Parents

TABLE OF CONTENTS

INTRODUCTION

———

Once upon a time, much of the world's art and science was made by the same people.

In the late 1800s, for instance, several people began to experiment with new photographic techniques. They realized that by taking many photos and displaying them in quick succession, they could simulate and accurately reproduce movement photographically. Soon enough, moving picture shows could be found in many places, and thousands of nickelodeon theaters opened.

Within a few short decades, motion pictures had become a major part of the entertainment industry. Every day, new film technologies were developed that made it possible for directors to realize more and more elaborate, realistic, and nuanced artistic visions. As they began to do so, the public and critics gradually began to accept film as more than just entertainment but art as well.

Film is an art form that owes everything to technology. The development of modern camera, lighting, audio recording, and special effects technologies have given filmmaking teams the tools they need to execute their vision as creatively and flexibly as possible.

But this isn't a book about film—at least, not specifically. This is a book about art—but also one about science.

Does the idea of mixing art and science seem a little strange to you? I wouldn't be surprised if it does. These days, most people perceive a significant dichotomy between the worlds of art and STEM (science, technology, engineering, and mathematics). It's hard to point to exactly the reason why, but I suspect that it begins in school. From a very young age, when children are asked what they want to be when they grow up, they are expected to give a single definitive answer. Among the acceptable answers to this question are "artist" and "scientist"—growing up to be an artist-scientist isn't an option. Not only is the separation between the two consistently highlighted, but there's also a general attitude that science is more important than art. This is reinforced by school curricula—science classes are always mandatory, and art classes are pushed off to the wayside, mere "electives" to be taken for fun rather than as preparation for any *serious* career.

This condescension toward the arts from people working in STEM fields is surprisingly ubiquitous. Ask yourself how many people you knew as a teenager who felt pressure from their parents to disengage from artistic pursuits to make room for STEM activities. People I knew in engineering school often called our university's College of Arts and Sciences the "School of Arts and Crafts."

The problem with this unspoken cultural bias is that it is arbitrary, self-sustaining, and incredibly limiting. Perhaps it is true, for instance, that most engineering jobs don't have a lot of room for artistic expression, and perhaps it is true that most graphic designers don't need to know calculus. Examine the dichotomy closely, however, and it begins to fall apart. Talk to most mechanical engineers, and you'll learn that they decided to pursue their careers because they loved to make things with their hands as children—you know, like sculptors and painters. Take a look at any large public art piece and ask yourself, was this assembled by some weirdo artist in her home studio or in a machine shop by experienced technicians?

A few hundred years ago, the world's great scientists, engineers, artists, and philosophers were all the same people. Leonardo Da Vinci, the Renaissance's ultimate Renaissance man, produced spectacular inventions and incredible paintings alike. Benjamin Franklin was both a gifted writer and a brilliant scientist. And animators of all sorts since the early twentieth century have constantly been developing new techniques, technologies, and software to advance their crafts.

Today, we find ourselves at the cusp of a new moment in history, one where advanced technology is now easier to use, learn, and access than ever before. Through recent endeavors like the Maker movement, the false dichotomy between STEM and art is being challenged once again.

As digital electronics become smaller and cheaper, and as new platforms are developed to help people learn to use them, vast new opportunities are opening in many different fields. One of these fields is art, and one of these opportunities is Arduino.

WHAT IS ARDUINO?

An **Arduino** is a little circuit board that makes it very easy to work with electronics.[1]

Arduinos work by making a special type of electronic chip called a "microcontroller" easier to program and connect to circuits.

"Arduino" is the name of a specific brand of a product like this, and many different models of Arduino circuit boards are sold. The **Arduino UNO** shown above (Italian for "one") has historically been the most popular model, although there are many shapes and sizes of Arduino boards.

You can connect electrical input components like switches, distance sensors, and touch sensors to allow the Arduino to react to the world around it. You can attach outputs like

---

1   Arduino is known as Genuino outside of the USA. In this book, the Arduino/Genuino company and electronics platform will always be referred to as "Arduino."

LEDs, speakers, and motors to allow it to flash lights, play music, and create motion in response to the information it collects from the outside world. Then, you can write code on your computer to tell an Arduino how it should control the outputs based on the information it receives from an input.

For instance, let's say we've connected this Arduino to a switch and a light.

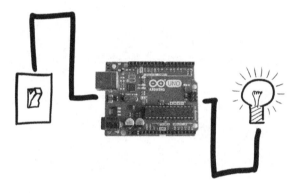

Now we can write some computer code and upload it to the Arduino to tell it how to interact with these two devices.

On the computer, we could write code that tells the Arduino to turn on the lightbulb if the switch has been flipped. Or we could do something even more clever, like tell the light to blink on and off at a certain speed and then to blink at a different speed depending on whether the switch is flipped or not.

Because of its relatively simple interface and coding language, Arduino is easy to learn to use but is still massively flexible and can be used to make many, many different things. This has led to it being popularly used in a wide variety of different fields—science, engineering, robotics, et cetera. But for the purposes of this book, the one we're going to concern ourselves with is one of its most popular but least considered uses: art.

ART AND ARDUINO

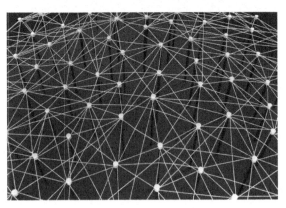

Above are two images of *Plural*, a 2019 work by Austrian design studio Mischer'Traxler that is installed at the Futurium museum in Berlin.[2]

For this installation, Katharina Mischer and Thomas Traxler created an intricate web of elastic strings, crossing back and forth over each other, and then attached them to pistons. Distance sensors were placed under the web to detect when a hand is above them. All of these were then connected to an Arduino programmed to raise the pistons near any distance sensor that detected the presence of an arm above it.

This very straightforward set of instructions creates an amazing effect when in action. The threads attached to each raised piston pull on every string they intersect, creating a dynamic moving web of strings.

Plural is one of a set of two pieces created by Mischer'Traxler as a commentary on the interconnectedness of the world and society. It physicalizes the social connections between everyone using overlapping strings. But even more fascinating than this basic concept is that in this work, the viewer is actually a part of the piece—not only are all the threads in the piece affected by the pull of all the others, but the viewer is the one who actually triggers this chain reaction.

Not only is the viewer causing a ripple effect throughout the entire network with a simple action, but it also isn't even an action that seems particularly consequential. She doesn't need to touch the web to have an effect on it. If the viewer makes any effort to interact with the piece, it remains stable. But if it remains stable, the viewer will never see the

2   Mischer'Traxler Studios, *Plural*, 2019, motors, elastic string, and
      electronics. Futurium, Berlin.

full depth of the work—she *must* interact with it in order to experience it, so to experience it, she must become part of the interconnected performance of the piece.

Because the designers of *Plural* decided to make the work interactive, the piece itself creates a metanarrative in which the viewer is not only the audience of the work, but also part of the work, and *also* a participant in its creation. Forget the composition of the piece. Forget about the use of color, material, negative space, everything you were taught to analyze in your art classes—the introduction of interactivity *alone* adds an entire fourth dimension to the analysis of the piece.

Just think—in Da Vinci or Ben Franklin's time, this work would have been impossible to create. But thanks to the advent of accessible digital technology, anyone could make it—even you.

Several years ago, I was hired to teach a summer STEAM (STEM + Art) program at the high school I had attended. For the first two weeks, I taught pure robotics, but for the final week of the program, I taught an experimental interactive art program. It had a few hiccups along the way, but by the end of the week, the kids got to learn to use Arduino to make art projects that used LED strips, computer graphics, and wearable electronics, topics no traditional STEM program would have ever been likely to touch.

While I was teaching, it struck me that I myself had never had the opportunity these kids were now getting. I certainly hadn't gotten it in engineering school, where despite majoring in both electrical engineering and design, I had never been asked to unify the two fields in any meaningful way. After all, the College of Engineering didn't mingle much with the "School of Arts and Crafts."

Art, design, and technology are not separate things. They've never really been separate things, and it's time to rewrite the narrative that says they are. In the right hands, with the right skills, artists and designers can use Arduino, electronics, programming, and plenty of other modern technology to add an additional dimension to their work.

This book is here to help you learn how to do that.

THE ELECTRONIC ARTIST'S TOOLBOX

Before we begin our journey into the wonderful world of electronic art, let's get familiar with the tools we'll be using the most during our journey. All of the projects in this book require a different set of electronic components, such as motors, LEDs, resistors, and LED strips, but in this chapter, we'll be looking at only the most essential tools for the job. I highly recommend acquiring all of these before working on any of the projects in this book.

THE ARDUINO UNO

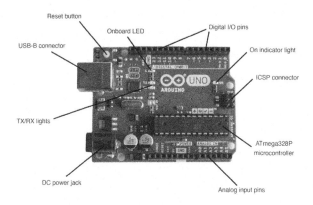

We'll be using the Arduino UNO for the projects in this book. There are many different models of Arduino board on the market, and many of them will also work with most if not all of the projects in this book. The UNO is the most popular and standard model of Arduino, however, so this book has been written with the UNO in mind.

The Arduino UNO, like all Arduino boards, is what is called a "microcontroller platform," a small circuit board that makes it very easy to build electronic circuits using a type of chip called a **microcontroller**. Microcontrollers are essentially very small, very weak computers. They don't have operating systems, so you can't easily interact with them as a user, but they can store memory and run programs. These programs can be used to control electronic inputs and outputs connected to the microcontroller and perform calculations using logic and math.

As it happens, this is more than enough capability for most electronics projects, and the small size and low price make microcontroller platforms an excellent choice for artists, makers, hobbyists, and professional engineers who want to quickly build and program circuits.

The Arduino UNO is built using the ATmega328P microcontroller. The ATmega328P is mounted in a socket on the top of the Arduino and can be easily removed and replaced with another ATmega328P for various purposes.

While most of the Arduino's technical capabilities are related to the ATmega328P, what makes microcontroller platforms such as the Arduino so useful is that they add extra components to the microcontroller to make them vastly easier to work with. Here's a short list of some of the important parts of the Arduino UNO's anatomy.

- USB-B connector—This makes it easy to connect the Arduino to a USB port on a computer so it can be programmed. Power can also be transmitted to the Arduino via the USB connector, making it easy to test out code without needing to connect external power.

- DC Power Jack—Allows the Arduino to receive external power via a DC power adapter, such as one you might use to power a speaker or a pencil sharpener.

- Digital I/O Pins—These connect to the various digital inputs and outputs on the microcontroller itself. They are designed to make it easy to connect and disconnect electronic wires and components to the Arduino.

- Analog Input Pins—These are similar to the digital I/O pins, but they allow the Arduino to read analog input signals instead of digital signals. They cannot output analog signals but can also be used as digital I/O pins in a pinch.

- On Indicator Light—Turns on when the Arduino is receiving power.

- TX/RX Lights—These will flash when the Arduino is sending or receiving serial data, including when a program is being uploaded to the microcontroller.

- Onboard LED—A built-in LED circuit that attaches to digital I/O pin 13. We'll use this in our first project and a few others as a quick and easy way to obtain visual feedback on how our code is working.

- Reset Button—Pressing this disconnects the microcontroller from power, resetting the device, and restarting whatever program is currently running.

- ICSP Connector—This stands for "In-Circuit Serial Programming" connector. This connector makes it possible to send and receive data from the Arduino using a more complex method that we won't cover in this book.

One last thing to note—the Arduino UNO is a completely open-source platform. This means that Arduino has released all of the schematics and design documents explaining how to make your own Arduino UNO, and it is legal and even encouraged for other people and organizations to do so. This means that there are many cheap "clone" Arduino UNO boards on the market, a lot of which are significantly cheaper than the name-brand model.

In my experience, brand-name UNO boards are tough, high-quality products that last a long time. However, they're not in everyone's price range, so I recommend also looking into clone models. They work basically identically to the name-brand model, and I've had good results with most of the clone models I've tried, although they can sometimes be slightly less reliable. In any case, I personally feel it's a good idea to have at least one name-brand model that you can rely on and a few cheaper clones that are cheap enough that you don't have to worry about breaking them.

USB A TO B CABLE

If you own a modern printer, chances are you have one of these lying around somewhere. One end of this cable is a standard male USB-A connector that you can plug straight into a USB connector on your computer. The other end is a male USB-B connector, which is boxier and slightly less common. These cables are often used to connect computers to printers, but they are also used to connect to the Arduino UNO and many other Arduino boards to program and power them. Many Arduinos come with them, but if you bought a cheap clone off of eBay or just the board itself, you would need to procure one yourself in order to complete any of the projects in this book.

WIRE STRIPPERS

Wire strippers are the most useful (if a bit adult-sounding) tools anyone working with electronics can have. I highly recommend getting a good pair that will last you a long time.

Wire strippers almost always include a blade to cut wires with, as well as several other features on the tool that let you crimp, manipulate, and strip the insulation off of electrical wire far more easily than you could with other tools. I prefer using strippers like the ones above, which are shaped like pliers, but they come in many shapes and sizes.

Wire strippers are designed to be able to strip the insulation off of several gauges (thicknesses) of electrical wire. In this book, we'll be using almost exclusively 22-gauge AWG solid-core copper wire, so pick out a pair with holes that are on the smaller size. In the pair shown above, the uppermost hole on the tip of the strippers is designed to strip 22-gauge wire. AWG wire gauges, the USA's standard method for measuring the diameters of different wires, use larger numbers to represent thinner wires, so if you can't find a pair that works with 22-gauge, err on the side of buying one that uses higher (thinner) gauges.

BREADBOARD

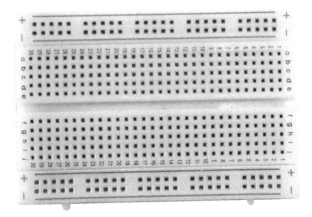

Breadboards are essential tools for prototyping electronics. They allow large numbers of small electronic components to be connected far more quickly and easily than anyone could possibly wire them all together using individual pieces of wire.

Breadboards take their names from literal wooden boards that people would put bread on. Back in the day, engineers would hammer nails into actual breadboards, attach their components to the nails, and then wrap pieces of copper wire between the nails to connect different parts of the circuit.

The image above shows a modern-day descendant of these wood-and-nail breadboards. They consist of a plastic case filled with holes, through which are strips of metal that connect groups of the holes in specific patterns. This makes it extremely easy to connect components together—all you need to do is push them into the right holes, and they'll be instantly connected. Disconnecting them is as simple as pulling them back out of the breadboard.

You won't need a breadboard for all of the projects in this book, and there are technically ways around using one at all during the projects to come, but I highly recommend picking up a small one about the size of the one in the image above to start with. I promise it will make your life easier.

THE ARDUINO IDE

```
// Blink
/* Turns an LED on for one second, off for one second,
 * and then repeats forever.
 */

int LED_PIN = 13;

void setup() {
  // put your setup code here, to run once:

  // set the LED pin to be an output
  pinMode(LED_PIN, OUTPUT);
}

void loop() {
  // put your main code here, to run repeatedly:

  digitalWrite(LED_PIN, HIGH); // turn LED on
  delay(1000); // do nothing for 1000 milliseconds (1 second)
  digitalWrite(LED_PIN, LOW); // turn LED off
  delay(1000); // do nothing for 1000 milliseconds (1 second)
}
```

The Arduino IDE (Integrated Development Environment) is the computer software that makes it possible to write code for your Arduino and upload that code to the board. We'll go over the minutiae of how the Arduino IDE works in the first project, but you should download it in advance and take a look at it to get prepared. The Arduino IDE desktop application is completely free and available for download at https:// www.arduino.cc/en/Main/Software.

If for whatever reason, you can't get the software running on your desktop, I also recommend checking out Arduino Create, an online service provided by Arduino that includes an in-browser version of the Arduino IDE. You can sign up for Arduino Create for free at https://store.arduino.cc/digital/create. The in-browser interface looks different from the desktop application, however, so it may be more difficult to follow along with some of the menu navigation if you use the web IDE.

PART 1

GETTING STARTED WITH ARDUINO

CHAPTER 1

YOUR FIRST ARDUINO SKETCH

———

Tools needed:

- Computer
- USB A to B cable

Parts needed:

- Arduino UNO (1)

It's time to write your first Arduino sketch! A **sketch** is the Arduino term for the code that you upload to the device in order to make it behave how you want it to.

Here's how this is going to go: I'm going to give you a series of steps to follow in order to make the sketch work. You will follow them. Once you've completed all of them and gotten this first project to behave how we want it to, we'll double back, and I'll explain the code line-by-line. Alright? All right. Let's dive in.

For this first sketch as well as the next one, I'm going to be a little more thorough in my explanation than I will be in later projects. It's important to have a strong understanding of the basics before moving on to more complicated topics.

The first project we're going to complete is very simple—we are going to make a light on the Arduino blink on and off. Essentially, the Arduino will act like a switch that we can control using some code.

The little holes on top of the black bars lining the edges of the Arduino are called **female header pins**, or just **pins** for short. They are used to attach electronic circuitry to the Arduino by allowing wires to plug directly into them. Each of these pins has a number to identify it, which is written in white right next to the pin.

In this sketch, though, we won't be attaching any wires to anything—instead, we're going to work with the Arduino's **onboard LED**, which is an LED light that is hard-wired to pin 13 on the Arduino (it's labeled with an L on the surface of the Arduino board). Because it's already connected to pin 13, we won't need to add any extra electronics.

1. Open the Arduino desktop application. If you haven't installed it yet, you can do so at https://www.arduino.cc/en/Main/Software

2. The window that opens should look something like this:

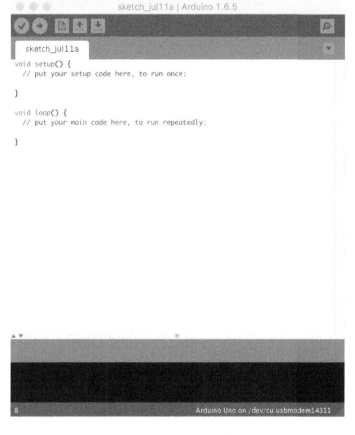

1. This is called the Arduino Integrated Development Environment (IDE) and is where you'll be writing all of your Arduino sketches. If the window that opens *doesn't* look something like this, or if no window opens at all, try the following to fix it.

– Click the "New" icon in the sketch window. To find it, first look at the checkmark button at the top left of the window. The "New" button is two buttons to the right of that one. Clicking the "New" button opens a brand new sketch with the default code already written.

– If you can't get the Arduino desktop application to work on your computer, register for an Arduino Create account at https://store.arduino.cc/digital/create and install the plugin it asks you to. This will allow you to use Arduino from your web browser. The window looks a bit different in Arduino Create, so it might be a bit harder to follow along, but all of the same buttons will be there in some form or other.

2. Type the following code into the sketch **by hand**. The reason you are typing it in by hand rather than copy-pasting it is that writing code efficiently is difficult and takes practice, mostly due to the fact that accidentally mistyping and breaking your code is easy to do and often difficult to realize you've done, so it's in your interest to begin practicing your code-writing accuracy right now. This code is written in a programming language called C++, which is a popular and powerful language related to C and similar to Java in many ways.

If you'd rather not type it in by hand, you can find all of the code used in this book at <web link>.

1. Go to File > Save (or press the button on the menu bar with an arrow pointing down) and save the sketch with the name "Blink" somewhere on your computer so you can easily find it again.

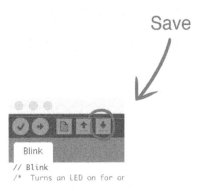

Save

Blink
// Blink
/* Turns an LED on for or

1. After you've saved, click the "Verify" button at the top left of the window (it looks like a checkmark) to verify the sketch.

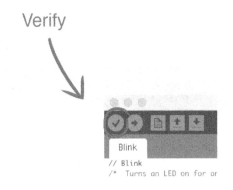

Verify

Blink
// Blink
/* Turns an LED on for or

1. This will tell the computer to process your sketch to see if there are any errors. The words "Compiling sketch…" should momentarily appear on the turquoise bar below the text area. If the bar below the text window turns orange, highlights one of the lines in red, and gives you

a strange error message in the place where it previously said, "compiling sketch," follow these troubleshooting steps; if it turns turquoise and says, "Done compiling," move on to step 5.

- In the event of a syntax error, the IDE should highlight a line of code in red. This indicates that the error is on or adjacent to that line (for instance, sometimes the error is on the line above). The error message that shows up written on the orange bar will provide a hint about what the error is. Sometimes the error message is complicated and hard to understand, but it is often useful in the event of a simple error.

- Ninety-nine times out of 100, Arduino coding errors are due to the omission of a semicolon. If money and circumstances permit it, I suggest you tattoo a semicolon on the back of your dominant hand, and maybe your forehead as well, to remind you of this. In the event of a semicolon error, the error message will read something resembling "expected ';' before '}' token" and highlight the line immediately after the one on which the semicolon is actually missing.

- Make sure that every line you've typed in is exactly identical to the code typed in the image above. Computer code can be very finicky about accuracy.

2. If your window says, "Done compiling," then it's time to upload your sketch. Take your USB A to B cable, and plug the "B" end into your Arduino Uno. Hold off on connecting the "A" end to the computer for now.

1. Now we have to make sure the computer knows what kind of Arduino board it's uploading to. Go to Tools > Board on the menu bar and select "Arduino Uno" from the rather lengthy list of possible boards.

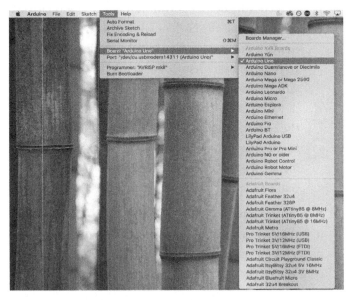

1. For the last step before we upload our code, we need to connect the Arduino to the computer and tell the computer which USB port the Arduino is attached to. The computer

will often connect to the correct port automatically, but let's make sure just in case. First, go to Tools>Port and look at the options it gives you. Take note of these options, then close the menu and plug the "A" (normal-looking) end of the USB cable into a USB port on your computer. Note that the port names on your computer may be different from the port names in this image.

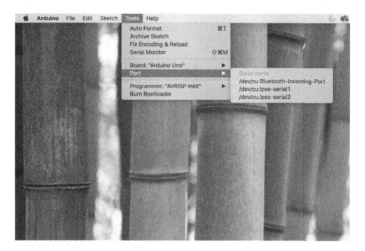

1. Now go back to Tools > Port. Notice how a new option has popped up, probably with the words "Arduino Uno" in parentheses next to it? Select that one.

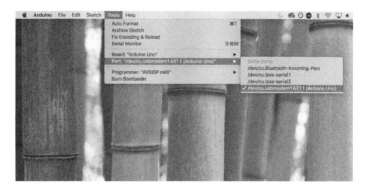

1. Upload the sketch by clicking the "Upload" button, which is directly to the right of the "Verify" button on the top left of the window and looks like an arrow pointing to the right.

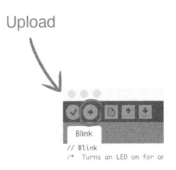

1. When it's done uploading, take a close look at the top of your Arduino board. The LED should be blinking on for one second, off for one second, and then turning on and off again in a loop. If it is not doing so, refer to step 7c.

The light should blink off...

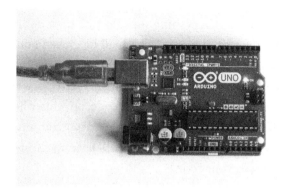

And then on, and then off again.

Congratulations! You've completed your first Arduino project! It doesn't do all that much, of course, but the things that make this simple little blinking light work make up the core principles of all Arduino programming.

Almost all of the projects we're going to work on after this find much of their foundation in this project. With that in mind, it's very important that we spend enough time on this project to understand it fully.

UNDERSTANDING THE CODE

Let's break it down line-by-line very, very carefully. The first line reads:

```
// Blink
```

This is what's called a **single-line comment**. A comment allows the coder to leave notes to themselves and others, label sections of code, and indicate the function of various sections of code.

To create a single-line comment, type two forward slashes one after the other. Everything on that line of code that appears after the two forward slashes will be grayed out by the IDE editor and ignored by the Arduino. In other words, anything you type in a comment after those two forward slashes have absolutely no effect on the code, no matter how profane or idiotic it is. (Keep in mind that if your comments are indeed profane or idiotic, they may still have an effect on anyone who reads your code.)

The next three lines are another type of comment:

```
/*   Turns  an  LED  on  for  one  second,  off
for  one  second,
```

```
 *   and  then  repeats  forever.
```

```
*/
```

This is a **multi-line comment**. A multi-line comment functions (or rather does not function at all) exactly the same as a single-line comment but can stretch across multiple lines. In order to create a multi-line comment, you have to open it with /* and close it with */. Anything after /* and before */, regardless of how many lines of code are between them, is ignored by the Arduino.

Note that when you begin typing a single line comment, the IDE automatically adds asterisks at the start of each new line until you close the comment to make it look pretty— these are not necessary for the Arduino to recognize them as comments. The code would work exactly the same if it were written like this:

```
/*   Turns an LED on for one second, off for
one second,
```

```
and then repeats forever.
```

```
*/
```

You could even move the "end comment" marker to the end of the second line, like so:

```
/*   Turns an LED on for one second, off for
one second,
```

```
and then repeats forever. */
```

There's a blank line after this comment (all blank lines are ignored by the Arduino), and then we have our first line of code that the Arduino will actually read. This is where things start to get interesting. The line reads:

```
int LED_PIN = 13;
```

This line creates, or rather, **declares** a variable. **Variables** are used to store values. However, any given variable can only store a certain **type** of value. What type of value it can store is determined when you declare the variable.

In this line, we declare a variable of the type int, name it LED_PIN, and assign it the value 13. When the Arduino reads this line of code, it creates a little space in its memory to store `int` values and puts the number 13 in that space. For the remainder of the code, when it encounters the term LED_PIN, it will check to see what value is stored in the space it made for LED_PIN. In this sketch, that value will always be 13 because that's the digital pin that the onboard LED is connected to.

The int variable type is short for "integer" and indicates that only integer values can be stored inside the variable. An int variable can hold any integer value, an integer being a number with no decimal points, such as 5, 0, 28, or 10,000. There is a size limit on the int type, however—it can only be used to store integer values between -32,768 and 32,767.

The second part of the statement, LED_PIN, is the name you're choosing for the variable. This can be almost anything, with a few restrictions. For example, you can't start your variable names with numbers, and they can't have any spaces or strange characters in them.

For variables that retain the same value for the entire duration of the code, the standard naming convention in C++, the programming language that Arduino programming is based on, is to make the name uppercase and to use underscores to separate words in the name.

You don't have to follow standard variable naming conventions if you don't want to, but it can be helpful to get in the habit of using them, so the code in this book will use standard conventions for variable naming, as well as other formatting. Regardless of how you name your variables, make sure any name you choose to use is descriptive enough about what it stores to allow you or someone else who might be reading your code to figure out what it's used for easily.

After LED_PIN, we have a single equals sign. When the Arduino sees an equals sign in the code, it knows that whatever number is on the right side of the equals is the number that should be stored in the variable named on the left side.

Finally, we have the value we're assigning to the variable, 13, followed by a semicolon (";"). **Do not forget the semicolon. Ninety-nine percent of all programming errors can be traced to forgotten semicolons.** The semicolon indicates to the compiler that a given statement has come to a close.

In summary, if you read the line

```
int LED _ PIN = 13;
```

as a sentence, it really just means "The integer called LED_PIN is equal to thirteen."

Next, let's first look at this entire block of code. A **block** is a portion of code bounded by "curly braces" (the '{' and '}' characters, respectively) that functions as a complete unit.

```
void setup() {

// put your setup code here, to run once:

// set the LED pin to be an output

 pinMode(LED _ PIN, OUTPUT);

}
```

Note that the information inside the block of code is indented—this is another formatting convention that the Arduino IDE encourages.

This entire block of code is called the **setup() function**. Every single Arduino sketch must have a setup() function. The role of setup() is to run code that initializes various things in the sketch. It runs all of the code between its open and closed "curly braces" one single time at the very beginning of the sketch and then never again until the Arduino is restarted. In its most basic form, the setup() function looks like this:

```
void setup() {

}
```

The setup() function above has nothing between its curly braces and thus does absolutely nothing. However, even if it does nothing, every sketch must have a setup() function, and every setup() function must look exactly as shown above, with a "void" initializer, the word "setup()" with the parentheses, and open and closed curly braces. Code may optionally go between the two curly braces, and there is almost always *something* between them.

In our code, we have three things between these brackets. The first two are just more comments.

```
// put your setup code here, to run once:

// set the LED pin to be an output
```

However, the last line is something new:

```
pinMode(LED _ PIN, OUTPUT);
```

This is something called a **function**. This particular function is called **pinMode()** and is built into the Arduino software. Functions are designed to, well, perform a specific function, and most have **parameters** that give them the information required to do their job. In the Arduino IDE, function names typically appear in orange, with the exception of setup()and loop(), which are special.

The function of pinMode() is basically to change one of the Arduino's settings. The Arduino UNO has an onboard LED that is connected to pin 13. We want to be able to turn this LED on and off by controlling whether power is moving through pin 13 or not. To do this, we must set the "mode" of pin 13 to OUTPUT. pinMode() allows us to set any pin to either the INPUT or OUTPUT mode, provided we tell it which pin to set the mode of and what mode to set it to. Thus, we give it the parameters by writing them in the parentheses that come after the function name like so:

```
pinMode(pin#, INPUT/OUTPUT);
```

In this case, the pin# is 13, and the mode is OUTPUT. However, we've already stored the pin number in the variable LED_PIN, so we can plug in the parameters as:

```
pinMode(LED _ PIN, OUTPUT);
```

The final block of code is called the **loop()** function:

```
void loop() {

// put your main code here, to run repeatedly:

 digitalWrite(LED_PIN, HIGH); // turn LED on

delay(1000); // do nothing for 1000 millisec-
onds (1 second)

digitalWrite(LED_PIN, LOW); // turn LED off

delay(1000); // do nothing for 1000 millisec-
onds (1 second)

}
```

The loop() function is another special function, like setup(), with the primary difference being that loop() will run all of the code between the curly braces from top to bottom, start at the top again once it reaches the bottom, and continue to loop this pattern until the Arduino is turned off. This is where most of the interesting parts of Arduino code can be found.

After the comment at the top of the block, we see a new function, **digitalWrite()**, as well as a single-line comment in a location we haven't seen one in before.

```
digitalWrite(LED_PIN, HIGH); // turn LED on
```

Single-line comments (or multi-line comments, for that matter) can begin anywhere on any line, even when that same line has code on it. Just keep in mind that anything at all, code or otherwise, that is written to the right of the slashes will be ignored by the compiler.

```
digitalWrite() is another function much like
pinMode, but instead of changing a setting,
it controls whether one of the Arduino's pins
is high or low. Its parameters are:

digitalWrite(pin#, LOW/HIGH)
```

The first parameter, the pin#, is the pin you want to control the output of. The second parameter is the output power level you want to set that pin to. Setting this parameter to LOW makes the pin output zero volts. Setting it to HIGH makes it output five volts (or whatever the highest voltage your board can output is). If we have a component, such as an LED, connected to that same pin, this allows us to control whether power is flowing through it and thus whether the LED is operational.

Therefore, the statement

```
digitalWrite(LED _ PIN, HIGH); // turn LED on
```

turns on the onboard LED connected to pin 13 (LED_PIN) by applying 5V of power across it.

The next line is as follows:

```
delay(1000); // do nothing for 1000 millisec-
onds (1 second)
```

The third and final function of this sketch, **delay()**, is even simpler than the first two. delay() causes the Arduino to pause everything it's doing and freeze for a given number of milliseconds (1 millisecond = 1/1000 second).

Why milliseconds? Milliseconds provide a higher degree of precision than seconds, and it's a unit of time that comes in very handy when using Arduino and electronics, which can process data many thousands of times faster than a human can. In fact, there is no variant of the delay() function built into Arduino coding that lets you use a larger unit of time than the millisecond, although there is one that lets you use a smaller unit of time. delay() has a single parameter: the number of milliseconds to delay everything for.

```
delay(milliseconds)
```

In our case, the parameter is 1000, which means that when the Arduino reaches this line of code, it will bring everything to a halt for 1000 milliseconds (AKA 1 second).

The last two lines of code inside the block look very similar to the first two:

```
digitalWrite(LED_PIN, LOW); // turn LED off
```

```
delay(1000); // do nothing for 1000 milliseconds
(1 second)
```

The only difference this time around is that instead of the second parameter for digitalWrite() being set to HIGH, it is now LOW, meaning that the Arduino will set the LED_PIN (pin 10) to LOW (0V), which will turn the LED off. It will then do nothing for a second. Once the Arduino has executed these final two lines, it will hit the end of the loop() function, as indicated by the curly brace at the end of the line of code, then go back to the top of the loop() and do everything all over again.

That was a lot to take in, so let me rewrite all of the code we just went through in English, so it makes a little more sense. This will be in the form that the compiler will read the code in, so I'll skip all the comments.

An integer-type variable with the name LED_PIN now has the value 13.
Begin the setup function:
LED_PIN, which is pin 13, is an output.
End the setup function.
Begin the loop function:
Set LED_PIN (pin 13) to HIGH (5V).
Do nothing for 1000 milliseconds (1 second).
Set LED_PIN (pin 13) to HIGH (5V).
Do nothing for 1000 milliseconds (1 second).
Go back to the beginning of the loop function.

That's really it. The code is read line by line, from top to bottom, executing each command in chronological order. The ultimate function of this code is found in the loop function:

1. Set LED_PIN to HIGH, which turns on the LED

2. Do nothing for one second, during which time the LED remains on

3. Set LED_PIN to LOW, which turns off the LED

4. Do nothing for one second, during which time the LED remains off

5. Go back to step one.

This process you've just undergone—writing a series of commands to tell a computer or Arduino exactly what you want it to do—is all coding really is. If you can understand this sketch, you're more than prepared to move on ahead.

EXTENDED LEARNING

Now that you understand how this sketch works, it might be helpful and fun to play around with the code you've already written to get used to writing your own code. Here are several simple ways you can modify the code we wrote in this project to make it work in new and interesting ways.

CHANGING THE LENGTH OF THE DELAY

What if you want your LED to blink faster? Simple: change the number in the delay() functions. The smaller the delay, the less time will pass between the light blinking on and blinking off. The larger the delay, the more time will pass between the light blinking on and blinking off.

To add an interesting twist, you could give each of the delay() functions a different parameter. If you make the delay after the light is turned on shorter than the delay after the light is turned off, what happens?

The answer is that it will turn on for a brief moment and then turn off for longer. The light will become just a little blip. Do the opposite, making the "on" delay longer than the "off" delay, and the light will flicker off occasionally.

Try changing the delay values, clicking the "verify" button (the check mark), and uploading your new code to the Arduino to see what happens.

CHANGING THE BLINK PATTERN

We've already written a sketch that turns the LED on, turns it off, and repeats. But what if you wanted a different pattern? What if you wanted to turn it on for a long time, turn it off for a long time, then rapidly turn it on and off before going back to the beginning?

If you want to increase the complexity of your blink pattern, you need to add additional digitalWrite() and delay() functions, with the appropriate parameters, to loop(). Everything inside the loop() will repeat, so as long as the code inside it is valid, it can be as long and complicated as you want it to be.

CHAPTER 2

YOUR FIRST ELECTRONIC CIRCUIT

———

Tools needed:

- Computer
- Wire strippers
- USB A to B cable

Parts needed:

- Arduino UNO (1)
- Breadboard (1)
- LED (1)
- 22 gauge solid-core hookup wire, various colors
- Resistor, 220Ω (1)

Now that we've had a solid introduction to the programming side of Arduino, it's time to take a look at the hardware side of things by connecting an external LED.

In electronics, **hardware** refers to all the physical parts of your circuit that connect to each other, while **software** refers to the intangible code instructions that we upload to the hardware so it knows what to do. Before we get into how the Arduino is able to electrically control this circuit, let's talk a little bit about the components we're using to make it.

WIRES

Wires are what humans use to control the flow of electricity. In nature, electricity can take many forms and flow in uncontrolled ways. When electricity moves through a wire, however, it must follow the path of the wire. In other words, wires do to electricity what pipes do to water: they funnel it to specific locations.

Wires come in many shapes and sizes, but in this book, we'll be using 22-gauge solid-core insulated copper wire. This type of wire is made of a thin length of copper coated in rubber. The copper conducts electricity, but the rubber doesn't, acting as an insulator and preventing the electricity from escaping the wire and flowing somewhere it isn't supposed to.

To use wires in electronics projects, you must cut the length you want from the spool they're typically sold in and then strip off the insulation from the ends so you can connect it to components and other wires.

RESISTORS

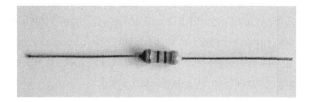

Resistors are some of the most important electrical components in existence. They add specific amounts of resistance to circuits, allowing the user to control exactly how much current is flowing through the circuit or a part of the circuit. Resistors come in many different resistance values (measured in ohms), which are indicated by their pattern of colored stripes.

LEDS

LEDs (short for light-emitting diodes) are a lot like tiny lightbulbs. They don't work in the same way as lightbulbs, but they do the same thing—they emit light. They're also much more energy-efficient than lightbulbs and produce a lot more light from a given amount of energy.

LEDs have two metal wires sticking out of them. These wires are called **leads** (pronounced "leeds"). One of the LED's leads is positive, and one is negative. The positive lead is almost always the longer one. In the wiring diagrams found in this book, a bent lead on an LED will always indicate the positive one. It's important to make sure the positive and negative leads aren't reversed. If electricity flows through an LED in the wrong direction, it can be damaged.

BREADBOARDS

Breadboards are tools used to make prototyping electronic circuits easier. Breadboarding is a midway point between just twisting wires together and attaching components together permanently.

Breadboards are designed to allow the user to quickly, easily, and temporarily connect electronic components together to test circuits. Rather than using individual pieces of wire to connect everything, it's often far easier to just hook up components to a breadboard.

Here's an image of a breadboard in use, with various wires and components attached to it:

Breadboards are covered in tiny holes that you can push components into. These holes are a lot like the pins on an Arduino. Underneath these holes are strips of metal that connect rows and columns in a predetermined pattern. For a small breadboard, that predetermined pattern usually looks something like this:

The lines in this image indicate which holes are electrically connected—if any two holes have the same line going across them, they are connected.

That means that if you wanted to connect, for example, a resistor to an LED, you could just connect them to two of the holes on the breadboard that are connected to each other. In the image below, the wire of the LED that is in the same column as the resistor is connected, just as if they were touching each other directly.

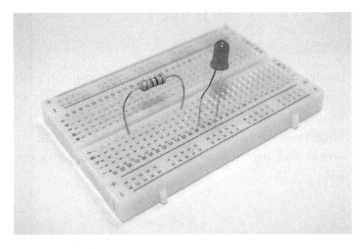

Breadboards usually have two rows each on the top and bottom that are connected along the entire length of the board (indicated by the blue and red lines in the diagram) and a bunch of columns in the middle. Keep in mind that these columns do not connect across the "channel" in the middle, even though the rows do connect across gaps. The rows on the top and bottom are usually connected to power and ground (the positive and negative ends of a battery, respectively), and the columns are used for components.

Many breadboards also have little terminals on the side (as can be seen in the first image of a breadboard) where external power and ground can be connected. Sometimes these even connect directly to the columns on the sides. Other times they don't. Make sure you know if the breadboard you're using has any special characteristics.

BUILDING THE CIRCUIT

Let's get started on our first circuit! From a programming perspective, this one will work almost exactly the same as the last one—the only difference is that instead of using the LED that's already attached to the Arduino, we're going to connect our own LED using wires, a resistor, and a breadboard.

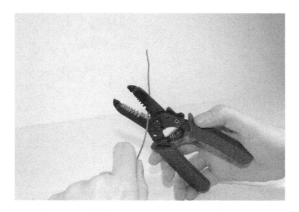

1. Using a pair of wire cutters/strippers, cut two small pieces of wire. Each wire should be a few inches long. The color of the wires doesn't matter, but I like to use different colors of wire to differentiate between different parts of the circuit.

2. Strip about half an inch of insulation off both ends of each small piece of wire using the wire strippers. To do this, close the "jaws" of the stripper around the little hole labeled "22" since you're using 22-gauge wire. If you don't have a hole with the label "22," use the hole labeled with

the number closest to 22. Using holes meant for higher gauges is preferable if you don't have a 22-gauge hole, since higher wire gauges equal smaller wire diameters.

1. Following this wiring diagram, attach an LED and a resistor to the breadboard, and then plug the wires you just cut and stripped into the pins on the Arduino labeled "10" and "GND." Then connect the other ends of these wires to the appropriate holes on the breadboard.

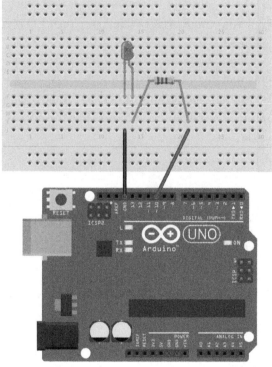

If your breadboard is bigger or smaller or looks a little different than the one in the diagram, no problem! All that matters is that any two wires that connect to the same column in the breadboard diagram are both connected to the same column on your actual breadboard. Which specific column they're connected to doesn't matter. For instance, the bent wire from the LED in the diagram should connect to the same column as one of the wires from the resistor.

Note that one of the little wires attached to your LED is slightly longer than the other. This longer wire corresponds to the slightly bent wire that the diagram shows attached to the LED. Make sure not to get the longer and shorter wire mixed up! You run the risk of damaging the LED if you put it in backward.

Also, note that there are several pins on the Arduino labeled "GND"—you can connect to any of these, and the sketch will still run fine. Once your circuit looks like this, you're ready to move on.

1. Now that the circuit is assembled, it's time to upload a sketch to the Arduino. The code below is nearly identical to the sketch we used before, except that this time, since the electronics we're using are connected to pin 10 instead of pin 13, LED_PIN is defined as 10.

```
// Blink
/* Turns an LED on for one second, off for one second,
 * and then repeats forever.
 */

int LED_PIN = 10;

void setup() {
  // put your setup code here, to run once:

  // set the LED pin to be an output
  pinMode(LED_PIN, OUTPUT);
}

void loop() {
  // put your main code here, to run repeatedly:

  digitalWrite(LED_PIN, HIGH); // turn LED on
  delay(1000); // do nothing for 1000 milliseconds (1 second)
  digitalWrite(LED_PIN, LOW); // turn LED off
  delay(1000); // do nothing for 1000 milliseconds (1 second)
}
```

Upload this slightly modified code using the same steps as you did in the previous project.

When it's done uploading, look at the LED on your breadboard. It should be blinking on for one second, off for one second, and then turning on and off again in a loop, just like the onboard LED did in the last project!

UNDERSTANDING THE CIRCUIT

Let's put together everything we've learned so far.

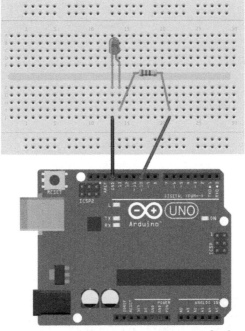

The breadboard is used to connect the Arduino, the wires, the LED, and the resistor together. When you upload the sketch to the Arduino, you're giving it a set of instructions for how and when it should supply power to this circuit.

Of course, you also have to supply power to the Arduino itself in order for any of this to work. Luckily, the USB connector takes care of this by using your computer as a power source for the Arduino. Arduinos can also be powered using external power sources and batteries, but we won't discuss that right now.

When the Arduino reaches the line of code that reads

```
digitalWrite(LED _ PIN,  HIGH);
```

it begins outputting +5 volts of electricity out of pin 10. This causes an electrical current to flow through the wire connected to pin 10 into the breadboard. The current then flows through the resistor, through the LED, and back into the Arduino via the wire connected to GND.

GND, otherwise known as **ground**, can also be understood to mean "o volts." All electricity wants to travel from a place with high voltage to a place with low voltage. Connecting pin 10 (which we've set to a voltage of +5V) to GND creates what is known as a "potential difference" that causes electricity to flow from the higher-voltage pin 10 to the lower-voltage GND pin.

Now that power can flow through the circuit, electricity will move from the Arduino, through the wire, and into the resistor. The resistor limits the amount of current that can flow through the circuit. If the current is too high, the LED won't be able to handle the stress and will quickly burn out.

After the resistor, current flows into the positive lead of the LED and is partially converted into light, causing it to glow. The current then flows out the negative lead, after which it returns to the GND terminal of the Arduino.

Electricity continues to flow for one full second while the Arduino waits for the delay(1000) function to end. Then comes:

```
digitalWrite(LED _ PIN,  LOW);
```

This sets the voltage of pin 10 to 0V, just like the GND pin. Now that there is no potential difference between the start and end of the circuit, electricity will no longer flow. With no electricity, the LED stops producing light.

The Arduino waits another second before reading the next line of code, then repeats the loop from the top.

That's the whole circuit! Now, it's time to use this circuit as the foundation for bigger and better things.

CHAPTER 3

ADDING A PUSH BUTTON

Tools needed:

1. Computer (1)
2. Wire cutters/strippers (1)
3. USB A to B cable (1)

Parts needed:

1. Arduino UNO (1)
2. Breadboard (1)
3. Normally-open push button (1)
4. LED (1)
5. 22 gauge solid-core hookup wire, various colors
6. Resistor, 1KΩ (1)

One of the most valuable ways Arduino can be used to enhance art and design pieces is by adding the dimension of interactivity to pieces. By adding components like sensors, switches, and buttons to art pieces, the invisible boundary between the audience and the work can be controlled, blurred, and even erased.

In this project, we're going to dip our toes into the water of interactivity by adding a **push button** to our first "blink" project. When the button is pressed, the Arduino's onboard LED will blink twice as quickly as before. When the button is released, the LED will continue blinking at the normal rate.

The anatomy of the push button we'll be using in this project is fairly straightforward. When you press the button, an electrical connection is created between the two leads on one side and the two leads on the other side. When you release the button, that connection is broken.

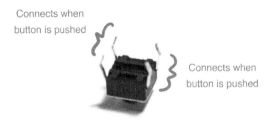

Connects when button is pushed

Connects when button is pushed

As shown in the image above, the two leads on the left that are bent in the same direction will connect when the button is pushed, and the other two on the right will do the same. This means that the way that the button is attached to the breadboard is important and will affect how the circuit functions. Keep that in mind as we get started with this project.

1. Connect your Arduino UNO, breadboard, push button, LED, four small segments of wires with stripped ends, and a 1KΩ resistor together as shown in this wiring diagram.

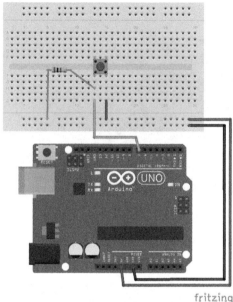

fritzing

A few things to note: The +5V pin that the red wire is connected to is similar to any of the other digital pins, except that it is always set to output. If we were to connect an LED to this circuit instead of a button, it would just always remain on. Many components require a constant power source to work. This is what the +5V pin is most commonly used for.

Also, notice that this time, we're connecting +5V and GND (0V) to the horizontal "rails." This is very common practice, and we'll be doing it throughout this book. Many breadboards have blue and red stripes along each of the rails to indicate which one is for GND (blue) and which one is for +5V (red).

Finally, it's very easy to position the button incorrectly. Make sure the wires attached to the button are positioned over the little channel in the middle of the breadboard. The little crooked ends of the leads should also point at each other across the channel.

1. Open up the Arduino IDE, create a new sketch, and type the following code in by hand. Once you're done, save the file as "Button" and click the "Verify" button (which looks like a checkmark) to make sure you typed everything in correctly. If you get an error message, follow the troubleshooting steps below.

   - Did the IDE highlight a line of code in orange? If so, your error is very likely to be either in this line of code or in the line above or below it.

   - Did you forget any semicolons?

   - Is all your code capitalized correctly and consistently?

   - Are all the "curly braces" there? If so, are they in the right places?

   - Is your code typed *exactly* as shown in the image?

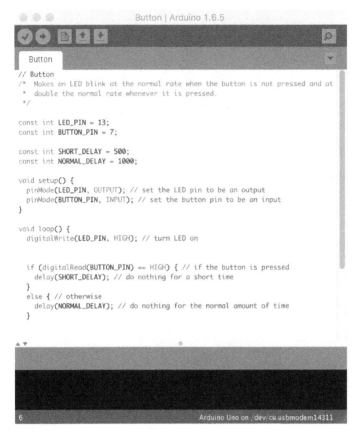

```
// Button
/* Makes an LED blink at the normal rate when the button is not pressed and at
 * double the normal rate whenever it is pressed.
 */

const int LED_PIN = 13;
const int BUTTON_PIN = 7;

const int SHORT_DELAY = 500;
const int NORMAL_DELAY = 1000;

void setup() {
  pinMode(LED_PIN, OUTPUT); // set the LED pin to be an output
  pinMode(BUTTON_PIN, INPUT); // set the button pin to be an input
}

void loop() {
  digitalWrite(LED_PIN, HIGH); // turn LED on

  if (digitalRead(BUTTON_PIN) == HIGH) { // if the button is pressed
    delay(SHORT_DELAY); // do nothing for a short time
  }
  else { // otherwise
    delay(NORMAL_DELAY); // do nothing for the normal amount of time
  }
```

When you're done, connect your computer to the Arduino with the USB A to B cable and upload the sketch. Once it's done uploading, the onboard LED should begin to blink on and off just like the external LED did in the last project.

Now press and hold the push button on the breadboard. If all goes well, the LED should blink twice as quickly as before. When you release it, it should return to its normal blink rate.

The onboard LED blinks slowly when the button isn't pressed.

When the button is pressed, the LED should blink twice
as quickly.

If the circuit doesn't work correctly, follow these trouble-shooting steps.

1. Make sure that you've wired up the breadboard exactly as shown in the wiring diagram. It might also be useful to trace the connections with your finger to make sure they follow the same patterns as the schematic.

2. Make sure your LED is facing the right way! The long (positive) wire should connect to the resistor, and the small (negative) wire should connect to GND.

3. Double-check your code. Even if the sketch verifies and uploads properly, sometimes a minor error can stop an entire sketch from running as intended.

UNDERSTANDING THE HARDWARE

Push buttons come in two main types: **Normally Open** (NO) and **Normally Closed** (NC). In a circuit, when a connection is "open," it isn't connected and current cannot flow, whereas when a connection is "closed," it *is* connected.

The type we're using in this project is a Normally Open button, meaning that *normally* (when it isn't being pushed), it's open (not allowing current to flow).

The inside of a normally-open push button looks something like this:

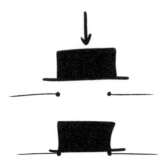

When the button isn't being pushed, there is no electrical connection between the two sides of the button, preventing current from flowing. When the button is pushed, the gap between the terminals is "closed," and current is able to flow through the button.

Normally-closed buttons are the opposite—*normally*, they're closed, but when the button is pushed, the button opens and interrupts the flow of current.

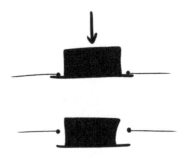

In this circuit, the button interrupts the connection between pin 7, which we declare to be an input in the code and the +5V pin. Because this button is NO (normally open), pin 7 and +5V are only connected when the button is pressed down.

In the sketch you uploaded, the Arduino checks to see if the button has been pressed or not by checking to see if pin 7 is receiving a HIGH (aka +5V) signal. It makes sense, right? Because pin 7 can only receive +5V when the button is pressed, the button must be pressed if pin 7 is receiving +5V.

There's also a resistor connecting between pin 7 and the button. What's that about?

In simple terms, this resistor guarantees that the Arduino can reliably tell when the button *isn't* pressed. If the resistor wasn't there, anytime the button isn't pressed, the pin would have no connection to any voltage at all. That makes the input pin susceptible to picking up random electrical static and thinking it's received a short HIGH signal even when the button isn't pressed.

Adding the resistor to connect the pin to GND means that pin 7 is always either connected to GND (which sends it a LOW signal) or +5V (which sends it a HIGH signal), removing any possible ambiguity and ensuring that your sketch always runs reliably.

UNDERSTANDING THE CODE

In the simplest terms possible, this sketch works by turning the LED on, changing the length of the delay based on whether the button is pressed, turning the LED off, and changing the length of the delay based on whether the button is pressed again.

Let's examine the parts of this sketch that we haven't seen before in some more detail:

```
const int LED _ PIN = 13;
```

This line is almost identical to the first line of code in the "Blink" sketch from the last chapter. However, this time we've added the word const in front of it. The **const** keyword is what's called a **variable qualifier**. Variable qualifiers change the behavior of the variable declared after it. const is short for "constant," meaning this variable never changes—it will always store the same value.

Putting the const keyword before the variable type when declaring a constant variable isn't strictly necessary, but it does use less of the Arduino's limited memory. For this reason, it's good practice to add const when you declare variables that won't change in value during the sketch.

The next line of code,

```
const int BUTTON _ PIN = 7;
```

does almost exactly the same thing as the first, except that it's declaring a name for a different pin, pin 7, which we've connected the button to. Thus the name "BUTTON_PIN."

In the last project, we had a delay() function that we used to add a pause before the button turned off again. However, we want the length of that delay to be smaller when the button is pressed, which will make the button blink more rapidly. We also want it to blink at its normal speed when the button isn't pressed. These seem like pieces of information that are going to be used more than once and that we might want to easily change later, so in the next few lines, we create some variables to store them.

```
const int SHORT _ DELAY = 500;
```

```
const int NORMAL _ DELAY = 1000;
```

In the setup() function, we set LED_PIN as an output, just like in chapter 1. This time, however, the line

```
pinMode(BUTTON _ PIN, INPUT); // set the button
pin to be an input
```

is also present. This specifies that BUTTON_PIN (pin 13) is an input and will be receiving electrical signals rather than sending them.

> *Note: because all pins are inputs by default, this line is unnecessary. If you want, you can delete this line and try uploading the sketch again—it shouldn't affect the project at all.*

The loop() function is where things start getting complicated. Inside loop(), we start off with the same digitalWrite() command we used in the last lesson, turning the LED on.

```
digitalWrite(LED _ PIN, HIGH); // turn LED on
```

But then we have to make a change. See, the delay() function that followed in the last sketch isn't necessarily going to be for the normal length of time. If the button is pressed, the delay should be half as long. So, instead of writing just delay(1000) like in the last sketch, we've added the following block of code:

```
if (digitalRead(BUTTON_PIN) == HIGH) { // if
the button is pressed

delay(SHORT_DELAY); // do nothing for a short time

}

else { // otherwise

delay(NORMAL_DELAY); //do nothing for the
normal amount of time

}
```

This is called an **if statement**. An if statement will only execute a specified block of code if a certain condition is true. This particular if statement also has an **else statement**, which executes a different block of code if that same condition is *not* true. Here's the basic format of an if statement:

```
if (conditional statement) {

code to execute if conditional statement is true

}
```

When an if statement also includes an else statement, it looks like this:

```
if (conditional statement) {

code to execute if conditional statement is true

}

else {

code to execute if conditional statement is
not true

}
```

The conditional statement can take many forms, but it typically uses a **comparison operator**, which is a little code "symbol" that tells the Arduino how two different numbers relate to each other. In this case, the comparison operator is "==", two equals signs next to each other. This is computer-speak for "equal to."

> *Note: it is critical that you type in two equals signs when using the "equal to" comparison operator. A single equals sign indicates variable declaration, not "equal to."*

In this case, the conditional statement is digitalRead(BUT-TON_PIN) == HIGH. **digitalRead()** is a companion to digitalWrite(), and it works in the opposite way. While digitalWrite() allows you to set a pin to HIGH or LOW, digitalWrite() tells you if any digital pin is receiving a HIGH or LOW signal from an outside source, such as our button. digitalRead() has one parameter: the pin to check the value of.

```
digitalRead(pin);
```

The entire function will set itself equal to HIGH or LOW, depending on the state of the pin it's checking. Using the "==" operator after it allows you to compare it to another value. Thus, our full conditional statement really means "the reading of BUTTON_PIN (pin 7) is equal to HIGH."

If this statement is true (e.g., if the button is pressed down, allowing voltage to fall across pin 7), then the code within the curly braces of the if statement will run. If this statement is not true (meaning the reading of pin 7 is LOW and the button is not pressed), it will not run the code within the if statement. The code within the if statement is nothing new—it just turns the LED on, as you saw in chapter 1.

The code inside the else statement also depends on the conditional statement—if the conditional statement is false (meaning the code within the if statement has not run), it will run the code within the curly braces of the else statement instead. In this case, this means that if the reading of pin 7 is *not* high, it will set the output level of pin 13 to low, turning the LED off.

Here's a diagram to make that a little easier to digest.

The rest of the code is pretty straightforward—the LED is turned on again with another digitalWrite(), and then an if-else statement identical to the previous one determines how long the delay should be.

That's it! Push buttons are super easy things to add to your projects to allow users to interact with them. In the next project, we'll be looking at another means of sending information to the Arduino—the Serial Monitor.

CHAPTER 4

THE SERIAL MONITOR

———

Tools needed:

- Laptop computer (1)
- USB A to B cable (1)

Parts needed:

- Arduino UNO (1)

There's still one major tool for working with Arduino that we haven't explored yet. This tool is called the **serial monitor,** which is a separate window on the Arduino IDE that allows you to send and receive messages from the Arduino while it's running. Not only is this invaluable for debugging complex code, but it also opens up the possibility of using a computer to control an Arduino and vice versa. This means that you could connect a light display to an Arduino and use your computer to control it in real-time or send input data collected by the Arduino back to the computer to control a digital display.

For now, however, the serial monitor is mostly useful to us because it can be used to test and debug code when you're not sure why it's not working. Imagine, for example, that you're trying to get an LED to light up, but for whatever reason, it doesn't work when you upload the code. If you tell the Arduino to send a message to the serial monitor whenever the LED is supposed to light up, you can check the serial monitor to see if the code that's supposed to be running is actually running. If the serial monitor receives a message when the LED is supposed to light up but doesn't, then the issue probably has to do with your wiring; if you don't receive a message, then it's likely that the code to light the LED up isn't triggering and needs to be rewritten.

The serial monitor uses serial communication to send and receive messages. **Serial communication** is like morse code for computers: By sending complex patterns of electric pulses through wires, you can transmit information from one place to another in the form of **binary code**, which is the computer language made up of ones and zeroes you've probably seen in the movies.

Serial data can be transmitted between a computer and another computer, between an Arduino and another Arduino, or between a computer and an Arduino. We'll cover all of these topics eventually, but in this project, we're going to start out by examining the latter and making a computer and an Arduino talk.

SENDING DATA TO THE SERIAL MONITOR

First, we'll be sending a string of text from the Arduino to your computer. There are no electronics needed for this—all you need to do is connect your Arduino to your computer using your USB A to B cable.

1. Plug your Arduino into your computer and upload the following code. Save it as "Serial_Write."

2. Once your code verifies and is working correctly, upload it to the Arduino.

3. Click the small magnifying glass-shaped icon in the top right corner of the Arduino IDE window.

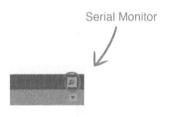

Serial Monitor

This opens the serial monitor, which allows you to view all of the serial information that the computer has received from the Arduino. The serial monitor window should look like this:

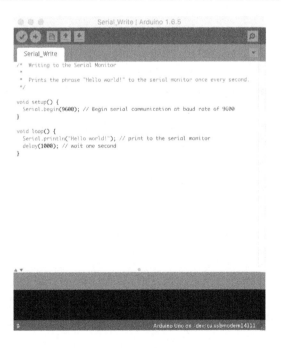

If all is working correctly, one new line of text containing the words "Hello world!" should be appearing in the monitor's display window every second. The first line might be messed up—that's just a minor display error that might occur and doesn't mean you did anything wrong.

UNDERSTANDING THE CODE

This is a very, very simple sketch. There are really only two lines of code that we haven't seen before.

First, in setup(), we have the line

```
Serial.begin(9600); // Begin serial commu-
nication at baud rate of 9600
```

For all intents and purposes, this is a function just like any of the other functions we've seen before, like pinMode() and digitalWrite(). But this one looks a little bit different because it has a period in the middle of it. There is a reason why it looks like this, but we won't discuss it right now—for now, just think of it like any other function.

Serial.begin() is a function that tells the Arduino to open up a connection to the serial monitor. You can't send or receive any messages via serial connection if you don't open up a channel for that communication to happen first.

Serial.begin has one parameter,

```
Serial.begin(speed)
```

where speed represents the speed at which serial data is transferred. This is also known as the **baud rate**, where **baud** means "the number of bits (ones and zeroes) sent per second." 9600 is a fairly standard baud rate for serial communication—you'll only need to change it if you're using serial communication for a very specialized purpose, such as exchanging data with an external device that can only run at a higher speed.

The next part of the code that's new comes in the loop():

```
void loop() {

Serial.println("Hello world!"); // print to
the serial monitor

delay(1000); // wait one second

}
```

Serial.println() is the second new function this code uses. You can probably guess what it does—it simply tells the Arduino to print a line of text to the serial monitor. It also has one parameter:

```
Serial.println(text)
```

where "text" is the text you want to print to the serial monitor. There is also a very similar function called **Serial.print()**, which does exactly the same thing as Serial.println() except that it doesn't automatically move on to the next line after it's done printing your message. This can sometimes be useful if you're trying to string together several pieces of text on the same line.

Note that the text "Hello world!" is enclosed in quotation marks in the code. The quotes tell the Arduino that the letters between them should be treated as text rather than a code command. The quotation marks are necessary—if you remove them and then verify the code, the code won't compile.

Finally, after Serial.println("Hello World!") we have a delay(1000) function. This is only here to make the Arduino pause before sending another line of text to the serial monitor. Try deleting it and re-uploading the code. Without the pause before the end of the loop, the Arduino will print to the serial monitor, immediately restart the loop, and print to the serial monitor over and over again, adding lines so quickly you can barely even read them. Feel free to delete the delay and reupload the code if you want to see what that looks like—it won't damage the Arduino. It'll just overwhelm you.

READING DATA FROM THE SERIAL MONITOR

Now that we can write to the serial monitor let's learn how to read from it. This process is a little bit more complicated, but not by too much.

1. Write the following sketch and upload it to your Arduino.

Open the serial monitor window on the Arduino IDE.

1. Click the text input box at the top of the window, type a capital letter A, B, or C, and either press "enter" on your keyboard or hit the "send" button next to the input box.

One of the three strings declared at the top of the code should appear in the serial monitor. Try experimenting with sending different combinations of letters and see what happens. For example:

- – What happens when you send three A's?
- – How about two C's and then a B?
- – How about if you send a D?
- – What about sending a lowercase letter?
- – What happens if you type multiple letters and send them all at the same time?

What you should find is that sending any combination of capital A's, B's, and C's will elicit a response from the Arduino, triggering it to output strings of text corresponding to the same letter as the capital letter you sent. Sending a lowercase letter, a capital letter that is not A, B, or C, or any character that is not a capital A, B, or C will elicit no response at all.

For example, here's the Arduino's response to receiving the letters A, B, and C one after the other.

UNDERSTANDING THE CODE

There's very little in this sketch that we haven't seen before, but there are more lines of code than we've seen in any other sketch so far. To understand it, let's break it down into chunks.

First, we have this:

```
// declare constant string variables for
use later
```

```
const String A = "This is string a.";
```

```
const String B = "This is string b.";
```

```
const String C = "This is string c.";
```

So far, we've talked about int variables, but we haven't discussed any other types. Now we have a new type: String. **String** variables hold "strings" of text. When assigning a string of text to a String variable, it's important to enclose the text inside double quotes, like this:

```
String variable = "This is a string
of text.";
```

The double quotes tell the Arduino that the text should be treated as a string variable rather than as code. This is also why we had to enclose the text in Serial.println() in double quotes in the last sketch. If the Arduino doesn't see them when reading the code, it won't understand what the purpose of the words in the string is and will fail to compile correctly.

These three String variables are used to store different strings of text that we'll use later in the code.

> *Note: you can use the const variable qualifier before any variable of any type. Because these strings aren't going to change anywhere in the program, we use the const qualifier when declaring them to save some memory in the Arduino.*

Next we declare a non-constant variable of another new type:

```
// declare empty non-constant char variable
to store data received
```

```
// from computer
```

```
char lastDataReceived;
```

The **char** type is similar to the String type, except that instead of storing a string of text, it can only store a single character, such as a letter or number.

Here we declare a char variable called "lastDataReceived" that we'll use to store characters later in the sketch. Right now, it's left empty, but if you wanted to declare a char variable and store a character in it at the same time, you'd do it like this:

```
char newCharacter = 'a';
```

For char types, we use single quotes (aka apostrophes) to let the Arduino know that the character we want to store in the variable is, in fact, a character. Keep in mind that **you cannot use double quotes to represent a character.** When the Arduino sees double quotes, it assumes that you're writing a string, and you can't store a string in a character variable. You can create a string that is one character long, but it's still a String type, and is not interchangeable with the chartype.

This sketch has exactly the same setup() loop as the previous one, with Serial.begin(9600) initializing serial communication between the Arduino and computer. The loop(), however, is very different.

```
void loop() {

if (Serial.available()) { // if the Arduino
has been sent any data

lastDataReceived = Serial.read(); // store
the sent data in lastDataReceived

if (lastDataReceived == 'A') { // if the
character 'A' has been received

Serial.println(A); // print string A

}

if (lastDataReceived == 'B') { // if the
character 'B' has been received

Serial.println(B); // print string B
```

```
}
```

```
if (lastDataReceived == 'C') { // if the
character 'C' has been received
```

```
Serial.println(C); // print string C
```

```
}
```

```
}
```

```
}
```

The first thing to notice about this code is that the entirety of the loop() is just one giant if statement with other things inside it. Let's ignore the stuff inside that if statement for now and simplify the code a bit:

```
void loop() {
```

```
if (Serial.available()) { // if the Arduino
has been sent any data
```

```
// the other code we're ignoring right now
goes here
```

```
}
```

```
}
```

Now we can home in on the meat of this if statement. Here we can see our next new function for this sketch: Serial. available().

Serial.available() is a little different than the other functions we've seen so far for two reasons: First off, it doesn't have any parameters, so you don't need to put anything between its parentheses (you still need the parentheses, though).

Second, unlike other functions, which take in information and perform a task, when you call Serial.available(), it performs a task and then returns a value. When a function **returns** a value, it essentially sets itself equal to that value. That value can then be assigned to a variable or compared to other things, just like any other value.

In the case of Serial.available(), the action it performs is to check if the Arduino has received any data from the computer. The value it returns is either TRUE if the Arduino has received data or FALSE if it hasn't. Thus, this if statement will only allow the rest of the code inside loop() to run if data has been received (i.e., if Serial.available() == TRUE).

So every time the Arduino checks to see if it's received any new serial data and finds it hasn't, it skips all the code inside the if statement, which also happens to be all the code in the loop. That means that as long as there's no new data, the loop() does absolutely nothing!

Why is it important to add this stipulation that the Arduino needs to have received data before we can actually perform any of the code? Simply put—in order to work with data, the Arduino needs to have data to work with first. Putting an input of nothing through the code can cause errors—it's much better to avoid dealing with that situation entirely.

But what if it *does* receive serial data from the computer? Well, in that case, it *will* run the code in the if statement, which looks like this.

```
lastDataReceived = Serial.read(); // store
the sent data in lastDataReceived
```

```
if (lastDataReceived == 'A') { // if the
character 'A' has been received
```

```
Serial.println(A); // print string A
```

```
}
```

```
if (lastDataReceived == 'B') { // if the
character 'B' has been received
```

```
Serial.println(B); // print string B
```

```
}
```

```
if (lastDataReceived == 'C') { // if the
character 'C' has been received
```

```
Serial.println(C); // print string C
```

```
}
```

The first line of this introduces the last new Serial function you need to know.

Serial.read() is similar to Serial.available in that it doesn't take any information—it just performs a task and returns a value. However, instead of returning TRUE or FALSE, it returns the first byte of serial data it has received. A **byte** is a unit of data size equal to eight bits. Incidentally, a char is exactly one byte of data.

So in this sketch, Serial.read() will return (i.e., be equal to) the next byte of serial data received. So if we look at this line:

```
lastDataReceived = Serial.read(); // store
the sent data in lastDataReceived
```

we can see that the Arduino will store the next character it receives via serial in lastDataReceived, which we declared as a char variable earlier in the sketch. Now the Arduino can use this character to decide what action to perform.

Following this variable assignment are three nearly identical if statements. They all work exactly the same way, but they use a different character and perform a slightly different action. The first one looks like this:

```
if (lastDataReceived == 'A') { // if the
character 'A' has been received

Serial.println(A); // print string A

}
```

This if statement checks to see if lastDataReceived (which is storing the last character received from the computer) is a capital 'A' character. If it, in fact, *is* a capital A character, we use Serial. println(A) to print the contents of string A to the serial monitor.

In the last sketch, we printed strings directly to the serial monitor by writing the words we wanted the Arduino to output inside the parentheses of Serial.println() and outputting them directly. Here, since we've already stored the string we want to output inside the variable A, we can just tell the Arduino to print A, and it'll know what to do.

And that's it! The next two if statements do exactly the same thing as the first one but instead check for the characters 'B' and 'C' and then print the contents of the corresponding string variable to the serial monitor. Because lastDataReceived only holds one character at a time, only one of these if statements can trigger on any given pass through the loop, ensuring that only the correct string is printed. If the last character received is neither 'A' nor 'B' nor 'C,' then none of the if statements will trigger at all.

One final note about this sketch: you may have observed that you can type several characters into the serial monitor's input box, such as "ABACCA" and send them all to the Arduino at the same time. Notice that doing this results in the same output you would expect from sending each character one by one.

This is because the Arduino is designed to handle receiving many characters of data very quickly. The Arduino has something in its main memory chip called the **serial buffer**, which is a section of its memory that is dedicated entirely to storing the serial data it has received.

The serial buffer can store 64 bytes of memory, which is the same as 64 characters. When the function Serial.read() is run, what it actually does is read just the first of those 64 bytes if any of them contain data. After it reads and returns the data so it can be used elsewhere in the code, it deletes the information that was stored in the buffer and pushes the next byte of stored data to the front of the line to be read next.

EXAMPLE: USING THE SERIAL MONITOR TO TROUBLESHOOT CODE

As I mentioned earlier, the serial monitor is very useful for troubleshooting Arduino code while you're testing it. For example, if I was developing the Blink sketch we wrote in the very first project, I might try writing it like this while I was testing it.

```
Blink_Testing | Arduino 1.8.13

Blink_Testing

// Blink (Testing Version)
/*  Turns an LED on for one second, off for one second,
 *  and then repeats forever.
 */

int LED_PIN = 10;

void setup() {
  // put your setup code here, to run once:
  Serial.begin(9600); // Begin serial communication at baud rate of 9600
  Serial.println("Running setup().");

  // set the LED pin to be an output
  pinMode(LED_PIN, OUTPUT);
}

void loop() {
  // put your main code here, to run repeatedly:
  Serial.println("Beginning of loop().");

  Serial.println("Turning LED on.");
  digitalWrite(LED_PIN, LOW); // turn LED on
  delay(1000); // do nothing for 1000 milliseconds (1 second)

  Serial.println("Turning LED off.");
  digitalWrite(LED_PIN, LOW); // turn LED off
  delay(1000); // do nothing for 1000 milliseconds (1 second)
}
```

22   Arduino Uno on /dev/cu.usbmodem14311

The only difference between this sketch and the original Blink sketch is the inclusion of a few Serial functions (and some blank lines for clarity). Oh, and there's an error in the code—if you typed this into your computer verbatim, it wouldn't work as intended.

In setup(), I've initialized the serial monitor with Serial.begin(9600) and added a Serial.println() that will print the message "Running setup()." to the serial monitor. Now when I run the sketch, I can open the serial monitor and see that the code is successfully running the setup() function. Now, this isn't extremely useful, as the Arduino will *always* run setup() if the code is capable of functioning, but it does let me know where the Arduino is in its execution of the code.

I've added a similar Serial.println() message at the beginning of loop(). Since this Serial.println() runs every time the loop resets, it prints a message every time the blinking pattern should restart. I've then added two more Serial.println() functions before each digitalWrite() function to tell me when the LED should be lighting up and when it should be turning off.

If I ran this code, I would immediately notice that the LED wasn't blinking on account of some error. However, if I hadn't written any of the serial commands in, I wouldn't immediately know whether the error was happening because I programmed it wrong or because the hardware was messed up.

But since I wrote in testing commands, I can open up the serial monitor, where I would see that every time I got a message reading "Turning LED on," the LED would not turn on. I know it's getting to that part of the code, and I know there isn't any issue with the LED turning off (since it's off all the time), so I can narrow down my search for the error.

First, I would probably check to see if the pin I'm outputting to is correct (which it is), and then I would reexamine the digitalWrite() command. And there I would find my error—I wrote LOW when I should have written HIGH, so the Arduino only ever turns the LED off and never on.

There are even more advanced applications of serial communication, but just the basics of them are extremely useful when it comes to troubleshooting and developing projects that use Arduino.

CHAPTER 5

FUNCTIONS

Tools needed:

- Laptop computer (1)
- USB A to B cable (1)

Parts needed:

- Arduino UNO (1)

Functions are incredibly powerful programming tools that form the foundation of most Arduino code. You've used plenty of pre-defined ones (such as pinMode() and digitalWrite() so far, but now it's time to make some for yourself.

Functions are very simple to make but are incredibly useful. A function that's only a few lines of code long can be enough to dramatically shorten some sketches and can make it very easy to do things that are very complex. This is especially true for projects that involve repeating patterns of movement, such as projects that use LED strips to create animated patterns or motors to create movement.

SOME GOOD TERMS TO KNOW

First, let's review what we already know about functions.

I previously described functions as named things in code that perform some action. Many functions have parameters, which are the pieces of information they need in order to do their job. Some functions return a certain value, which means that when it's finished doing its job, the function sets itself equal to some value. This value can then be used in calculations, compared to other values, or stored in a variable.

Now it's time to learn how functions work in a little bit more detail.

First, I want to add a few new terms to your programming vocabulary. The first of these is "argument." **Arguments** are the specific pieces of data you give a function so that it can do its job. How is an argument different from a parameter, you might ask?

Parameters are the pieces of data the function *needs*. When a function is created, the programmer has to determine exactly what pieces of information the function will need in order to run. They must then create variables within the code of the function to store this input information. These pieces of information are the function's parameters.

Arguments are the other side of that equation—they're the actual values that the function is *given*. When you see a function "called" (meaning "used") in a piece of code, such as digitalWrite(ledPin, HIGH), the arguments are "ledPin" and "HIGH." ledPin could have any of several different values, and HIGH is a specific value, but in both cases, they actually give information to the function for it to use.

In casual conversation, the terms are often interchangeable, but it's good to know the precise difference before you start making your own functions.

The second thing you should understand is the concept of return types. A function's **return type** is the type of value it will return, whether it be int, char, String, or something else. This is the type of value a function sets itself equal to when it finishes doing its job.

Let's say we were trying to use a hypothetical function called getValue(). If getValue()'s return type was int, we would have to keep that in mind when calling it in our code. For instance, this variable declaration would work:

```
int newVariable = getValue();
```

while this variable declaration would not:

```
char newVariable = getValue();
```

Because its return type is predetermined, getValue() will always return an integer variable, such as 12, or 300, or 6. That means that you can assign whatever value it returns to an integer variable with no issues, but trying to assign it to a char variable will result in an error.

Many functions don't actually return any value at all—for instance, both pinMode() and digitalWrite() do indeed perform a task, but they don't set themselves to any value to be used elsewhere in the code. Trying to assign the value of either of these to a variable will produce a similar error because you would be asking the Arduino to set a variable equal to a value that does not exist. These types of functions are said to have a "void" return type.

YOUR FIRST FUNCTION

We've spent a lot of time so far working with functions that the Arduino developers defined for us in advance. These mostly perform important, direct tasks relating to the Arduino's inputs and outputs, as well as serial communication. Now it's time to make a function of your own.

This is the bare minimum structure of a user-defined function with no parameters:

```
void functionName() {

// code for function to run when called

goes here

}
```

This looks awfully familiar, doesn't it? That's right—it's formatted exactly the same way as setup() and loop()!

Essentially, practically *all* of the programming we've done so far has really just been defining the setup() and loop()functions. When the Arduino boots up and begins running, it first calls setup(), and then it calls loop() over and over again until you disconnect the device from power. If you want to make another function of your own, you can do so by formatting it in exactly the same way and picking any valid name for it.

All functions must be defined outside of the loop statement. If we wanted to add a user-defined function to a typical sketch, we'd have to add it in like this:

```
void setup() {

}

void loop() {

void functionName() {

}
```

You can define these three functions in any order, although I personally prefer to define setup(), then loop(), then all user-defined functions.

As you can see from all three of these functions, the four major things every function definition requires are as follows:

1. The function's return type—This can be any of the value types in the Arduino language.

2. The function's name—The rules about what names a function can have are similar to the rules about which names a variable can have—no strange punctuation, symbols, or spaces. It's standard to name functions using the same camel case convention used for naming non-constant variables.

3. Open and closed parentheses at the end of the function name—If your function has no parameters, just leave them blank, like this: ().

4. Open and closed curly braces—Between these open and closed curly braces, you can write all the code that your function will run when called. You don't have to write anything inside them at all, but the function will do nothing if you don't.

As an example, here's a modified version of the "Blink" sketch that moves the contents of the loop() statement into a separate function called blinkLED(). Upload it to your Arduino and watch what happens.

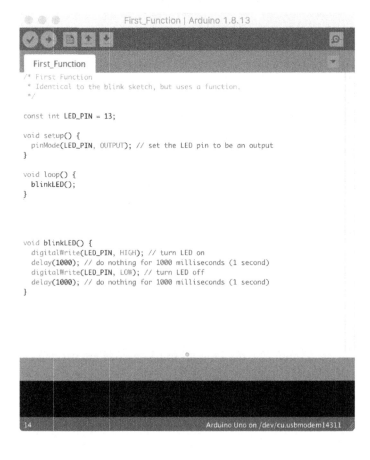

```
First_Function | Arduino 1.8.13

First_Function
/* First Function
 * Identical to the blink sketch, but uses a function.
 */

const int LED_PIN = 13;

void setup() {
  pinMode(LED_PIN, OUTPUT); // set the LED pin to be an output
}

void loop() {
  blinkLED();
}



void blinkLED() {
  digitalWrite(LED_PIN, HIGH); // turn LED on
  delay(1000); // do nothing for 1000 milliseconds (1 second)
  digitalWrite(LED_PIN, LOW); // turn LED off
  delay(1000); // do nothing for 1000 milliseconds (1 second)
}
```

14   Arduino Uno on /dev/cu.usbmodem14311

So what happens when you run this code? The LED will blink on for a second, then off for a second, and then repeat, just like the first blink sketch did.

The sketch runs exactly the same as normal, except that now the first and only statement in the loop() is blinkLED(). This tells the Arduino to find the function named blinkLED(), then run all of the code enclosed between its curly braces line by line.

When all the code inside blinkLED() is done running, the code returns to where the function was first called in loop()and goes to the next line. Since there actually is no next line, the loop() restarts and immediately runs blinkLED() again.

And that's about all you need to know to start writing your own functions!

But let's think about this a little more. We could have just as easily left all that code in the loop() function, and it would work exactly the same. In fact, it's a little more complicated to have to define an entirely new function to do something so simple. So how can we make this function even more useful?

STREAMLINING YOUR CODE WITH FUNCTIONS

Here's another sketch to illustrate how functions can be incredibly powerful tools for writing complex codes quickly and efficiently.

We've done something different with the blinkLED() function this time. If we look at the first line of the function definition, we've added something between the parentheses:

```
/* Variable Blink Function
 *
 * Uses a function to easily vary the length of time it takes to blink the
 * onboard LED.
 */

const int LED_PIN = 13;

void setup() {
  pinMode(LED_PIN, OUTPUT); // set the LED pin to be an output
}

void loop() {
  blinkLED(1000);
  blinkLED(5000);
  blinkLED(200);
  blinkLED(200);
}



void blinkLED(int delayTime) {
  digitalWrite(LED_PIN, HIGH); // turn LED on
  delay(delayTime); // do nothing for delayTime milliseconds
  digitalWrite(LED_PIN, LOW); // turn LED off
  delay(delayTime); // do nothing for delayTime milliseconds
}
```

```
void blinkLED(int delayTime) {
```

You may recognize this as a variable declaration. What we're doing in this version of the function is declaring an int-type parameter variable that we can use throughout the rest of the function to alter how it runs.

If you notice, we've added a few more function calls in the loop() this time:

```
void loop() {
```

```
blinkLED(1000);
```

```
blinkLED(5000);
```

```
blinkLED(200);
```

```
blinkLED(200);
```

```
}
```

Each of these also has a value in between the parentheses of the function call. These values are the arguments that will be passed to the delayTime variable when the function is called. In other words, when the Arduino sees this:

```
blinkLED(1000);
```

it knows to run this:

```
void blinkLED(int delayTime) {
```

```
digitalWrite(LED _ PIN, HIGH); // turn LED
on
```

```
delay(delayTime); // do nothing for delay-
Time milliseconds
```

```
digitalWrite(LED _ PIN, LOW); // turn LED off
```

```
delay(delayTime); // do nothing for delay-
Time milliseconds
```

```
}
```

and set the value of delayTime to 1000 in every instance where the variable appears.

Now the actual number of milliseconds used in the delay() functions inside blinkLED() depends on the argument in the function call. This means that every time you call the function, you can tell the LED to blink for a different amount of time.

For instance, in blinkLED(1000), the LED turns on, waits for 1000 milliseconds, turns off, and waits for 1000 milliseconds. But in the very next function call, blinkLED(5000), 1000 milliseconds becomes 5000 milliseconds, i.e., 5 full seconds. In the very next two calls, we get two very brief flashes that only stay on for 200 milliseconds and only stay off for 200 milliseconds, i.e., one-fifth of a second.

Now we've made our blink pattern much more complex with only a few extra lines of code. But here's the real question: is it worth making a new function to do all of this?

To find our answer, take a look at a rewritten version of this code (left) next to the original (right). This will make the LED blink in exactly the same pattern as the previous sketch but doesn't use a function to do it. There's no need to type all this out yourself—just take a look at it.

```
● ● ●          Variable_Blink_Without_Function | Arduino 1.8.13
```

Variable_Blink_Without_Function

```
/* Variable Blink Without Function
 *
 * Blinks the LED on for a second, off for a second, on for five seconds,
 * off for five seconds, and then on and off for a fifth of a second twice in
 * a row.
 */

const int LED_PIN = 13;

void setup() {
    pinMode(LED_PIN, OUTPUT); // set the LED pin to be an output
}

void loop() {
    digitalWrite(LED_PIN, HIGH); // turn LED on
    delay(1000); // do nothing
    digitalWrite(LED_PIN, LOW); // turn LED off
    delay(1000); // do nothing

    digitalWrite(LED_PIN, HIGH); // turn LED on
    delay(5000); // do nothing
    digitalWrite(LED_PIN, LOW); // turn LED off
    delay(5000); // do nothing

    digitalWrite(LED_PIN, HIGH); // turn LED on
    delay(200); // do nothing
    digitalWrite(LED_PIN, LOW); // turn LED off
    delay(200); // do nothing

    digitalWrite(LED_PIN, HIGH); // turn LED on
    delay(200); // do nothing
    digitalWrite(LED_PIN, LOW); // turn LED off
    delay(200); // do nothing
}
```

```
15                                        Arduino Uno on /dev/cu.usbmodem14311
```

```
● ● ●                  Variable_Blink | Arduino 1.8.13
```

Variable_Blink

```
/* Variable Blink Function
 *
 * Uses a function to easily vary the length of time it takes to blink the
 * onboard LED.
 */

const int LED_PIN = 13;

void setup() {
    pinMode(LED_PIN, OUTPUT); // set the LED pin to be an output
}

void loop() {
    blinkLED(1000);
    blinkLED(5000);
    blinkLED(200);
    blinkLED(200);
}


void blinkLED(int delayTime) {
    digitalWrite(LED_PIN, HIGH); // turn LED on
    delay(delayTime); // do nothing for delayTime milliseconds
    digitalWrite(LED_PIN, LOW); // turn LED off
    delay(delayTime); // do nothing for delayTime milliseconds
}
```

```
20                                        Arduino Uno on /dev/cu.usbmodem14311
```

Look at the difference! The version of the code that uses the function uses fewer lines of code, less space, and is way easier to read. And this is just to turn the LED on and off four times—imagine if we needed to do it 100 times!

RETURN FUNCTIONS

There are only a few more things that are useful to know about functions before we move forward.

Let's write a short function that does simple math. This function will be called multiplier() and will multiply two numbers together. Unlike our last functions, this one will actually return a value (the result of the two multiplied numbers) and will also take more than one parameter (the numbers to multiply together).

Note: There's a chance that the number the serial monitor outputs might accidentally duplicate. You should see the number 6, but it might write it twice and say 66. To avoid this, open the serial monitor before you upload your sketch to the Arduino.

Let's begin by looking at the function definition at the end of the sketch.

```
int multiplier(int num1, int num2) {

int product = num1 * num2;

return product;

}
```

First, note that we didn't write void multiplier—because we want this function to return the product of two numbers so that it can be used elsewhere in the sketch, we have to define a different return type. So, we instead say int multiplier to tell the Arduino that it should expect this function to return an integer value once the function is done running.

Second, because this sketch requires two parameters, we simply declare two different parameter variables separated by a comma, int num1 and int num2. When the function is called and two arguments are passed to the function, the value of the first argument will be stored in num1 , and the value of the second argument will be stored in num2.

Inside the brackets of the function definition, we only have two lines of code. First is this:

```
int product = num1 * num2;
```

This creates a new integer variable called product and sets it equal to the value of num1 times num2.

Note: the asterisk is the symbol for multiplication in code. We'll go over more of the details of how math works in programming as we encounter it.

Essentially, all this line does is take the two values the function is given for num1 and num2, multiplies them together, and stores them in an integer variable called product.

The next line has something new in it.

```
return product;
```

The **return** command is used to return a value or the value of a variable. If your function has a type other than void, it *must* have a return command in the function definition, or you'll get an error.

In this function, the value of the variable product is returned. That means when the function is called in the sketch, the function will set itself equal to whatever value product has when it is returned.

The last piece of this puzzle is setup().

Note: loop() is left empty in this code since we only want to do the math once.

PART 1: GETTING STARTED WITH ARDUINO

```
void setup() {

Serial.begin(9600);

// assign the product of 2 and 3 to a
variable called "result"

int result = multiplier(2, 3);

Serial.println(result);

}
```

The meat of this setup() function is this line in the middle:

```
// assign the product of 2 and 3 to a
variable called "result"

int result = multiplier(2, 3);
```

This line declares a new variable called result and assigns it the value of multiplier(2, 3). When multiplier(2, 3)is called, the Arduino finds the definition of the multiplier() function and passes the values 2 and 3 to the variables num1 and num2 respectively. The function then calculates the product of 2 and 3, which is equal to 6, and then returns that value. Thus, the value of the variable result is set to 6. Finally, the Serial.println(result) command then prints this value to the serial monitor.

WRITING MULTIPLE FUNCTION DEFINITIONS

There's one last quirk of how functions work that we haven't talked about yet. Functions like multiplier() are written so that they require exactly two arguments when the function is called in order for it to work. But many functions will still work if you call them using different numbers of arguments.

Here's an example of how to write a version of the multiply() function that accepts either two or three arguments.

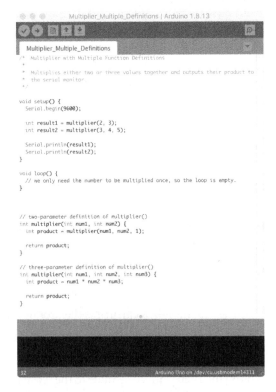

In this sketch, the products of two different sets of numbers are calculated using multiplier() and printed to the serial monitor. However, we've added a new function definition that allows us to call multiplier() using either two or three different arguments.

First, take a look at the second definition of the function:

```
// three-parameter definition of multiplier()

int multiplier(int num1, int num2, int num3)  {

int product = num1 * num2 * num3;

return product;

}
```

You might think that this definition should be more complicated, but it really isn't. It's almost exactly like the definition from last time, except that there's a new parameter, num3, that gets multiplied during the declaration of product.

The new two-parameter declaration, however, is where things get interesting:

```
// two-parameter definition of multiplier()

int multiplier(int num1, int num2) {

int product = multiplier(num1, num2, 1);

return product;

}
```

What's going on here? Well, simply put, when the two-parameter function is called, all it does is pass off the actual calculation to the *other* definition of multiplier(), the one with three parameters. However, the third argument is 1. Because any number times 1 is itself, this does the same thing as multiplying num1 * num2.

The three-parameter definition returns the correct value, which is then assigned to product and returned as normal. Now, when using the function in your code, you can either multiply two or three numbers.

That's about all there is to know about functions! Later on, in this book, we'll begin working with LED strips that can display very complex lighting patterns. In our exploration of these LED strips, functions are going to become indispensable in allowing us to simplify very complex code into just a few lines, so it's good to understand them sooner rather than later.

PART 2

MOTION

CHAPTER 6

INFRARED DISTANCE SENSORS

———

Tools needed:

- Laptop computer (1)
- Wire cutters/strippers (1)
- USB A to B cable (1)

Parts needed:

- Arduino UNO (1)
- Breadboard (1)
- Sharp GP2Y0A21YK0F IR Distance Sensor (1)
- LED (1)
- 22 gauge solid-core hookup wire, various colors
- Resistor, 150Ω or greater (220Ω recommended) (1)

Distance sensors are electronic devices that can tell an Arduino how far away an object is. They're used quite frequently in robotics to help robots avoid obstacles, but they have also found a home in art, where they're commonly used to sense where a viewer is in relation to the art piece. The piece can then respond dynamically based on this information.

The designer Juraj Kotian created his piece *Reflection of the Age* as a commentary on *mammon*, the "excessive desire for wealth." The work explores the consequences of modern media culture's emphasis on the rich and famous and how it can lead to average people becoming obsessed with attaining the largely unreachable ideal of immense material wealth.[3]

Distance sensors were a natural choice for physicalizing that struggle. In the piece, a distance sensor is used to determine

---

3   Juraj Kotian, *Reflection of the Age*, 2015, aluminum, polystyrene, ultrasonic range finder, Arduino MEGA, electrical wires.

how close the viewer is to the polystyrene balls that make up the sculpture. As the viewer reaches toward them, the balls reach toward the viewer as well. But when the viewer reaches too close, the balls suddenly pull away, almost like the fruit and water in the Tantalus myth.

There are two common types of distance sensor.

- **Infrared distance sensors** (also known as IR distance sensors) allow you to calculate the distance between the sensor and an obstacle by sending out a pulse of infrared (IR) light. The light then bounces off the surface of the obstacle and returns to the sensor. The sensor measures the angle at which the IR light returns to approximate the distance from which it bounced back. IR distance sensors tend to be somewhat imprecise, so they're most useful for measuring the presence or absence of an obstacle rather than obtaining highly accurate distance calculations.

- **Ultrasonic distance sensors** allow you to calculate the distance between the sensor and an obstacle by sending out a pulse of extremely high-pitched ultrasonic sound (so high-pitched, in fact, that humans can't hear it). Kotian uses two of these in *Reflection of the Age*. The sound then bounces off the surface of the obstacle and returns to the sensor. The sensor measures the time elapsed between transmitting the pulse and the pulse returning to the sensor. Because sound travels at an approximately constant speed on earth, the elapsed time can then be used to calculate the distance between the obstacle and the sensor. Programming ultrasonic distance sensors are a little bit more complicated because the timing has to be measured very precisely, but the advantage is that they tend to be more accurate and have a longer range.

Infrared distance sensors are somewhat easier to use and understand and are easier to implement for smaller projects, so we'll be working with one of them.

A Sharp GP2Y0A21YK0F IR Distance Sensor.

1. Before assembling the circuit, make sure your IR distance sensor is properly connected to its wires. Depending on exactly which distance sensor you have, you may be able to attach wires that come with the sensor using a little white snap connector called a Japanese Solderless Terminal (JST) connector. Make sure to securely snap the white connector attached to the wires into the white receiver on the IR sensor before you continue onward.

2. If yours doesn't come with a JST connector, you may need to attach wires manually. In the image above, I used some wires I had that ended in female header pins that I could easily push onto the three leads from the sensor—you may have to be more creative in attaching longer wires to the leads if you don't have these. I recommend stripping wires, wrapping them around each lead, and then attaching them more securely using electrical tape.

3. Follow this wiring diagram to connect your circuit to the breadboard. The red (rightmost) wire should connect to +5V, the black (middle) wire should connect to GND, and the green (leftmost) wire should connect to analog pin A0.

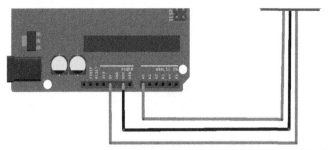

fritzing

1. Upload the following sketch to your Arduino.

```
// IR Distance Sensor
/* Turns an LED on when a distance sensor senses that something
 * is a certain distance away from it.
 */

const int LED_PIN = 13; // connects to LED
const int SENSOR_PIN = 0; // connects to distance sensor signal pin
int distance; // stores distance value received from distance sensor

void setup() {
  pinMode(LED_PIN, OUTPUT); // set the LED pin to be an output
  pinMode(SENSOR_PIN, INPUT); // set the distance sensor pin to be an input

  Serial.begin(9600); // begin serial communication
}

void loop() {
  distance = analogRead(SENSOR_PIN); // stores reading in distance variable

  if (distance > 200) { // if something is near the sensor
    digitalWrite(LED_PIN, HIGH);
  }
  else { // if something is not near the sensor
    digitalWrite(LED_PIN, LOW);
  }
}
```

2. If everything works correctly, the LED should turn on when you bring your hand close to the LED, and it should turn off when you move it farther away.

The LED is off when there's nothing in front of the sensor...

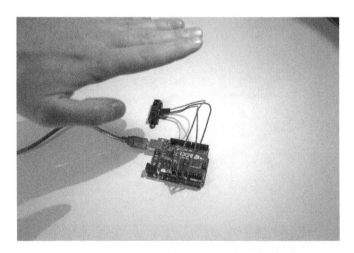

...and then turns on when you bring your hand close!

UNDERSTANDING THE HARDWARE

The electronics setup for this project is relatively simple. The only component is the IR sensor, which has exactly three wires.

- The red wire supplies power to the IR sensor so that the device can operate.

- The black wire grounds the IR sensor so that it forms a complete circuit with the Arduino.

- The green wire is used by the distance sensor to send the Arduino information it has collected about the distance of the closest object in front of the sensor.

This model of IR sensor is not highly accurate and can only sense things that are a few feet away from it, but for the purposes of this code, it works well. All we need to know is if something is close enough to the sensor to trigger the LED— we don't need specific measurements.

ANALOG AND DIGITAL COMMUNICATION

Up until now, we've only received and transmitted digital information (HIGH or LOW, on or off, 1 or 0), so we've only been using the Arduino's digital pins (pins 0-13). However, the Arduino UNO also has a set of analog pins, which is what we're using in this project. Pins A0-A5, each of which is marked with the letter "A" to indicate that it's an analog pin, can receive analog data. However, unlike how the digital pins can both receive and transmit digital data, they can only receive analog data and cannot transmit it.

But what exactly do "analog" and "digital" mean? They're terms we throw around a lot in day-to-day life, but it's very rare to hear anyone actually define them.

That one friend of yours who listens to obscure indie music and never hesitates to show off her vinyl collection might use the word "analog" while talking about record players and cassette tapes. That really annoying kid you went to college with who never shut up about Bitcoin might use the word "digital" pretty often. Both might somewhat accurately say that "analog" technology is a few decades older than "digital" technology, and that "digital" technology is what computers use, while "analog" technology is what people used until DVDs became more popular than VHS tapes.

These answers aren't exactly wrong, but they still fall short of answering what exactly each of those words means.

In essence, "analog" and "digital" are two different methods used to transmit information.

- **Analog** communication is the transfer of information by using a large spectrum of possible values within a range.
- **Digital** communication is the transfer of information by using one of two possible different values.

Almost all electronic devices have to store and transfer information by using electricity. Electricity cannot be formed into words like human language, so electrical and computer engineers have had to develop other means of working with information.

Electrical devices communicate by controlling the amount of electricity that is being sent at any given time. Most of the time, the "amount" of electricity is really the amount of voltage being applied. If we were to graph the amount of voltage being received via an analog input over time, such as one of the Arduino's analog input ports, it could look something like this:

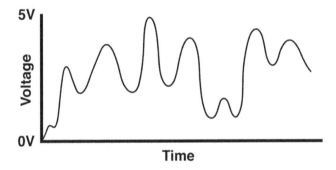

The receiver, in this case, the Arduino, can read exactly what each voltage value is and then interpret what each voltage value means. For instance, if the device sending the information was a temperature sensor, then "0V" could mean "0° C", "5V" could mean "100° C", and any given voltage in between 0V and 5V could refer to some value in between these.

Now, if the information were being transferred *digitally* to one of the Arduino's digital input pins, the input would look considerably different:

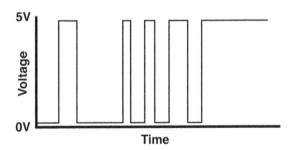

This is the primary difference between analog and digital communication: Analog communication uses a range of possible values, while digital communication can only use two different values: high and low.

"High" is usually +5V. "Low" is usually 0V. Any voltage value in between is rounded to +5V or 0V. It's useful, however, to think of the ideas of "high" and "low" from a more conceptual standpoint, as the actual terminology used to define them can change. In binary computing, for instance, these same two values are referred to as "0" and "1", corresponding to "low" and "high," respectively. "Off" and "on" are another way of saying "low" and "high."

In this sketch, the distance sensor is transmitting analog information to pin A0 on the analog pin. We can then write code that interprets that analog information.

UNDERSTANDING THE CODE

This sketch begins like any other. First, we define our pins and other variables.

```
const int LED_PIN = 13; // connects to LED

const int SENSOR_PIN = 0; // connects to
distance sensor signal pin

int distance; // stores distance value
received from distance sensor
```

In this sketch, we have a third variable that is declared differently from the others: int distance. There are three things to note about this variable:

It has no const keyword, so this variable can (and does) change elsewhere in the sketch. It is perfectly acceptable to make some variables constant by adding const while making other variables not constant.

Because it is not constant, the naming convention is different. This variable uses the same style of capitalization as many of the functions you've seen (such as pinMode() or digitalWrite()), where all the words in the name are smushed together, and the first letter of every word(except for the first!) is capitalized. This is often called **camel case** because the capital letters kind of look like a camel's hump. Naming variables using this convention is technically optional, but it's generally standard to name variables that change throughout the sketch like this.

Note that the distance variable has no assigned value! It is necessary to assign a value to a variable in order to use it, but *it is not necessary to assign the value at the same time as it is declared*. Right now, this line of code merely says that an integer variable named distance exists. It has no value yet.

In setup(), LED_PIN is declared to be an output while SENSOR_PIN is declared to be an input.

```
void setup() {

pinMode(LED _ PIN, OUTPUT); // set the LED
pin to be an output

pinMode(SENSOR _ PIN, INPUT); // set the
distance sensor pin to be an input

}
```

As usual, the loop() statement is where things get more interesting.

```
void loop() {

distance = analogRead(SENSOR_PIN); //
stores reading in distance variable

if (distance > 200) { // if something is
near the sensor

digitalWrite(LED_PIN, HIGH);

}

else { // if something is not near the
sensor

digitalWrite(LED_PIN, LOW);

}

}
```

The first line of loop() sets the value of the variable "distance" to equal the reading received from the sensor pin.

```
distance = analogRead(SENSOR_PIN); //
stores reading in distance variable
```

This is the moment in the code where we actually assign a value to the variable distance. Because we're not creating it here (we declared it at the beginning of the sketch), we don't need to include its type, so the type declaration int is nowhere to be found. The value we are setting it to is the value returned by the function analogRead().

analogRead() is similar to digitalRead() except that:

1. It can only be used with the analog input pins, and
2. Instead of returning HIGH or LOW, it returns an integer analog value between the numbers 0 and 1023.

analogRead()'s sole parameter is:

```
analogRead(pin)
```

where pin is the analog pin number to read data from.

One thing to note: The reading returned by analogRead() will be roughly proportional to the distance to the nearest object measured by the sensor *but not numerically equivalent to it.*

If the value received is 300, it does not mean the obstacle is 300 inches or 300 feet or 300 centimeters away from the distance sensor. Rather, the closer the object is, the higher the reading will be. The farther the object is, the lower the reading will be. It is possible to approximate what reading the sensor will give for specific distance values, but for this sketch, we just want to know when the sensor is close to an object, not when it's a specific distance away from something.

The second part of the loop is an if-else statement.

```
if (distance > 200) { // if something is
near the sensor
```
```
digitalWrite(LED _ PIN, HIGH);
```

```
}
```

```
else { // if something is not near the
sensor
```

```
digitalWrite(LED _ PIN, LOW);
```

```
}
```

Here we use a greater than (>) sign to check to see if the value of distance is greater than 200. The less than (<) sign also exists and works very similarly but isn't seen in this sketch.

Because the value of distance is updated to the current distance sensor reading every time the loop restarts, it might be greater than 200 during some cycles and less than 200 during other cycles. When distance is greater than 200, the comparison is true, and the block of code inside the if statement is run.

```
digitalWrite(LED _ PIN, HIGH);
```

This turns the onboard LED on.

When distance is less than 200, the comparison is false, so the block of code inside the else statement runs instead.

```
digitalWrite(LED _ PIN, LOW);
```

This turns the onboard LED off.

For this distance sensor, lower analog values indicate a greater distance from the sensor, and higher analog values indicate a nearer distance to the sensor. So, if the analog reading increases above 200, it means that the object must be close to the sensor, so the LED turns on. If it dips below, it must be farther away, so the LED turns off.

If you want to extend this project, try changing the threshold value (currently 200) at which the light will turn on. Increasing the value will make the LED turn on only when the sensor is closer to an object, and decreasing the value will make the LED turn on only when the sensor is farther from an object.

CHAPTER 7

PLAYING WITH DC MOTORS

———

Tools needed:

- Laptop computer (1)
- USB A to B cable (1)
- Wire cutters/strippers (1)

Parts needed:

- DC motor (1)
- Battery, any size (1)
- 22-gauge solid-core copper wire
- Arduino UNO (1)

DC motors are probably what you think of when you imagine a motor. Here's a photo of one.

DC stands for **direct current**, the type of electrical circuit most often used in small devices and in conjunction with Arduino. A direct-current circuit is any circuit where the direction of current flow remains constant. Some kinds of circuits are **alternating current (AC)** circuits, where the direction of current changes many times per second. AC circuits are useful for a lot of reasons, but most of them have little to do with Arduino, so we won't talk about them here.

All DC motors have three main parts: the wires that supply it with power, the body of the motor where the electromagnetic magic that makes motors work happens, and the motor shaft, which is the part that rotates.

If you've never used one before, it's good to get to know your DC motor before you start trying to use it.

Try taking a piece of scotch tape and making a little flag around the motor shaft, like so:

This will make it easier to see which direction the motor is turning. You can attach anything to the motor shaft that you can get to stick properly, provided the motor is strong enough to actually turn it.

Now, find an alkaline (or rechargeable!) battery lying around somewhere. It can be any kind of battery at all—AA, AAA,

9V, whatever. All batteries have two contacts—a positive contact, usually indicated by a plus sign, and a negative contact, indicated by a minus sign. Touch one of the motor's wires to one of these contacts and the other wire to the other contact.

If the wires are properly connected to the motor, the battery is not dead, and the motor is not broken, the motor shaft should begin spinning rapidly, whipping the little tape flag around with it. Neat, huh?

Now try switching the wires between the battery contacts. The shaft should begin spinning in the opposite direction.

Fundamentally, that's all a motor does—it turns in one direction or the other. There are other factors, of course, that determine its speed, measured in **RPM** (rotations per minute), and its **torque** (rotational force, which determines how much weight it can rotate). The voltage and current applied to the motor are among the most important of these factors, and we can cleverly manipulate them with an Arduino to control the behavior of the motor.

Let's try connecting your motor to your Arduino to see if we can control its speed.

1. If you haven't yet, fold a piece of tape around the motor shaft to act as a little flag. This will make it easier for you

to tell how quickly and in which direction the motor is spinning.

2. Attach the motor to GND and pin 11 on the Arduino as shown:

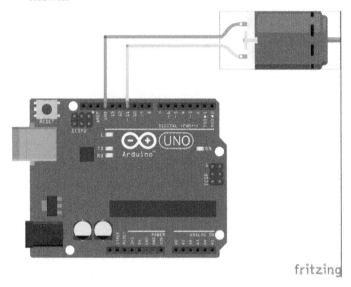

fritzing

You can attach either wire to either of the two pins—it'll just change the direction that the motor will rotate, which doesn't matter for this test. The color of each wire also doesn't matter for this project.

1. Type the following code into the Arduino IDE and save the sketch as "DC_Motor."

```
/* DC motor
 * Accelerates a DC motor once every two seconds until it reaches maximum speed,
 * then decelerates it every two seconds until it stops.
 */

const int MOTOR_PIN = 11;

void setup() {
  pinMode(MOTOR_PIN, OUTPUT);
}

void loop() {
  // accelerate the motor
  analogWrite(MOTOR_PIN, 64);
  delay(2000);
  analogWrite(MOTOR_PIN, 128);
  delay(2000);
  analogWrite(MOTOR_PIN, 192);
  delay(2000);
  analogWrite(MOTOR_PIN, 255);
  delay(2000);

  // decelerate the motor
  analogWrite(MOTOR_PIN, 192);
  delay(2000);
  analogWrite(MOTOR_PIN, 128);
  delay(2000);
  analogWrite(MOTOR_PIN, 64);
  delay(2000);
  analogWrite(MOTOR_PIN, 0);
  delay(2000);
}
```

If everything is working correctly, your motor should begin
turning, bump its speed up several times (once every two
seconds), bump its speed down several times, and repeat
the cycle.

UNDERSTANDING THE CODE

We start off by declaring a constant integer variable—this
time, we name it MOTOR_PIN because this time we're connecting a motor, and we set its value to 11 because that's the
number of the pin we're connecting the motor to.

```
const int MOTOR _ PIN = 11;
```

In setup(), we use pinMode() to set MOTOR_PIN to an output just like we did with the pin for the LED.

```
void setup() {

pinMode(MOTOR _ PIN, OUTPUT);

}
```

In loop(), we use delay(2000) a bunch of times to tell the Arduino to hold off on changing anything for two full seconds between every command.

```
void loop() {

// accelerate the motor

analogWrite(MOTOR _ PIN, 64);

delay(2000);

  analogWrite(MOTOR _ PIN, 128);

delay(2000);

analogWrite(MOTOR _ PIN, 192);

delay(2000);

analogWrite(MOTOR _ PIN, 255);

delay(2000);
```

```
// decelerate the motor

analogWrite(MOTOR_PIN, 192);

delay(2000);

analogWrite(MOTOR_PIN, 128);

delay(2000);

analogWrite(MOTOR_PIN, 64);

delay(2000);

analogWrite(MOTOR_PIN, 0);

delay(2000);

}
```

The only new thing to understand about this sketch is the inclusion of a new function. **analogWrite()** is to analogRead() as digitalWrite() is to digitalRead(): Instead of reading data from analog inputs like analogRead(), analogWrite()gives you the ability to output a range of analog values to a component. This means that instead of just turning components on and off, you can dynamically alter *how much* they are turned on. This gives the Arduino the ability to finely control things like the speed of a motor or the brightness of an LED.

analogWrite() has two parameters:

```
analogWrite(pin#, outputValue)
```

The pin# is the number of the pin to output an analog signal from. The outputValue is the analog value you would like to output.

Much like the input values from analogRead(), there is a range of finite values that analogWrite can output. However, this range is narrower than the range of values that can be read—you can only output values from 0 to 255, with 255 representing +5V, 0 representing 0V, and the numbers in between indicating voltages in between those two values.

Congratulations! You have now learned how to use digitalWrite(), digitalRead(), analogWrite(), and analogRead(), the four horsemen of Arduino input/output programming.

In this sketch, we use analogWrite() to control the speed of the motor by outputting different values between 0 and 255, with two-second delays in between each output. The higher the value, the higher the voltage applied to the motor, and thus the faster the rotation speed.

The first half of the loop() writes higher and higher analog values to the motor until it caps out at 255. The second half then brings it back down again until it hits the floor at 0V, stopping the motor entirely.

And that's that on DC motors! DC motors are very useful for motion that doesn't have to be extremely precise. For example, a piece of a sculpture that needs to rotate continuously or as part of a gear system that makes something move back and forth in a straight line.

ONE LAST NOTE ABOUT ANALOG OUTPUTS

There's one last thing I should mention about analogWrite(). See, the thing is, outside of a few exceptions, most Arduino boards can't actually produce true analog outputs. They can read and write digital signals, and they can read analog signals, sure, but they can't actually output other voltages besides a digital HIGH signal and a digital LOW signal. That means that if you write analogWrite(MOTOR_PIN, 128) and expect it to output +2.5V because 128 is about half of 255, that isn't actually what's going to happen.

What the Arduino does instead of actually producing an analog output is to find a workaround that effectively produces the same result in most cases. This workaround involves something called **pulse-width-modulation** (PWM).

Here's how PWM works: When an "analog" output command is sent to a pin that can use PWM (indicated by a squiggly line next to the pin number), the pin will output a digital HIGH for a certain length of time and then output a digital LOW for a certain amount of time, modulating this length based on the analog value needed to be transmitted. The effect this has is to average out the HIGH and LOW signals to effectively become something in between.

For example, think of a digital output such as an LED. If a PWM signal was sent to an LED, the Arduino would turn the LED on and then off and then back on again hundreds of times per second. When you look at an LED, since it's actually turned off part of the time, your eyes will essentially average out the high and low light levels, and the LED will appear to be less bright.

On 100 percent of the time.

On 50 percent of the time.

On 0 percent of the time.

Ultimately, even though the LED isn't turned on at half power in the middle photo, it looks like it is because, *on average*, less than the full voltage *is* being supplied to the LED. It's just that if you paused it at any given moment, it would either be fully on or fully off.

CHAPTER 8

PLAYING WITH SERVO MOTORS

Tools needed:

- Laptop computer (1)
- Wire cutters/strippers (1)
- USB A to B cable (1)

Parts needed:

- Arduino UNO (1)
- Tower Pro Micro Servo (1)
- 22 gauge solid-core hookup wire, various colors

Servo motors (just servos for short) are a special type of motor. Instead of turning continuously, servos will turn to any specific position you tell them to rotate to. This makes them highly useful for any project that requires things to move with a small but highly precise range of motion.

Servo motors can be found in machines used in many industries in some form or another. For artists, servo motors are often used in projects like kinetic sculptures or animatronics.

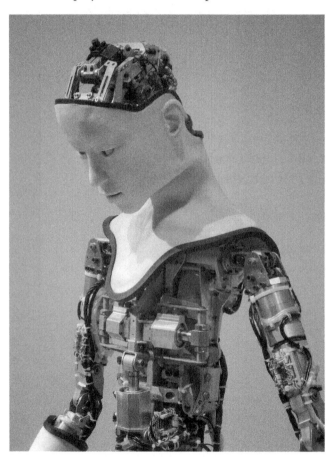

This project will familiarize you with how to control servo motors with an Arduino.

1. If it isn't attached, screw the little plastic "arm" that comes with the servo onto the little metal piece on the servo. In the image below, the "arm" isn't shaped like a single plastic "arm" at all but rather a cross shape. Servos often come with multiple attachable arms so that you can use whichever one works best for your project.

2. Connect your servo motor to your Arduino, as shown below. If your servo has female header pins at the ends of its wires, cut three short wires and strip both ends, then connect one of the wires to each header pin. Some servos have slightly different color schemes for their wires, so it's a good idea to look up the part number of the servo you're using and verify with a datasheet. For the Tower Pro Micro Servo used in the image below, the yellow-ish-orange wire should connect to pin 9, the red wire should connect to the +5V pin, and the brown wire should connect to one of the GND pins.

1. Upload the following code to your Arduino.

```
Servo_Motor | Arduino 1.8.13

Servo_Motor
// Servo Motor

#include <Servo.h>

Servo servo;

void setup() {
  servo.attach(9);
}

void loop() {
  // wipe arm from 0 to 1 degrees
  for (int pos = 0; pos <= 120; pos++) {
    servo.write(pos); // set servo position to current value of pos
    delay(20);
  }

  // wipe arm from 120 to 0 degrees
  for (int pos = 120; pos > 0 ; pos--) {
    servo.write(pos); // set servo position to current value of pos
    delay(20);
  }
}

                                    Arduino Uno on /dev/cu.usbmodem146201
```

1. If all goes well, the little plastic arm should begin to wipe back and forth.

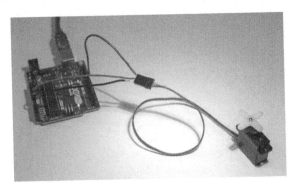

The arm starts in one position...

...then slowly rotates 120 degrees, and then rotates back.

UNDERSTANDING THE CODE

Arduino comes with a servo library pre-installed, which makes it very easy to control servo motors. This library is appropriately named "Servo."

```
#include <Servo.h>
```

As with all libraries, in order to use the added functions, we first have to create a named Servo object.

```
Servo servo;
```

We've named our Servo type object "servo," so now in order to control the physical servo, we can simply use the name "servo" to send commands to it.

Now that we've created the object, we have to tell it which pin we've physically connected our servo to so it knows where to send its commands. We do this using the servo.attach() method.

```
void setup() {

servo.attach(9);

}
```

servo.attach() has only one parameter: the pin that the servo is connected to. In this case, this is pin 9.

```
servo.attach(pin)
```

Our loop() is divided into two parts: one to wipe the servo forward, and one to wipe the servo backward. Let's start by taking a look at the first half:

```
void loop() {

// wipe arm from 0 to 1 degrees

for (int pos = 0; pos <= 120; pos++) {

servo.write(pos); // set servo position to
current value of pos

delay(20);

}
```

servo.write() is a method that moves the servo to a position between 0 and 180 degrees, or more if your servo supports more than 180-degree movement. It has one parameter: the position (in degrees) to rotate to.

```
servo.write(position)
```

Most servos, even very cheap ones, can rotate up to about 180 degrees. The cheaper ones will sometimes get a little fidgety near 180 degrees, however, so it's usually good to avoid rotating the full 180 degrees if you aren't using a higher-quality servo.

This part of the loop() increases the position that the servo is being rotated to by one degree every iteration of the loop, from 0 degrees to 120 degrees. Note that instead of using the < operator in the condition, this for loop uses <=, less than or equal to, meaning that the final value of pos will be 120 rather than 119. After the position is updated, there is a very short delay of 20 milliseconds to slow down the speed of rotation.

The second half of the for loop does basically the same thing, just in reverse.

```
// wipe arm from 120 to 0 degrees

for (int pos = 120; pos > 0 ; pos--) {

servo.write(pos); // set servo position to
current value of pos

delay(20);

}

}
```

Now the position variable starts at 120, decrements by 1 every iteration of the loop, and terminates when pos equals 0. This rotates the shaft backward one degree at a time.

That's about all you need to know to control servos! Seriously, it's that simple. Just connect the servo, tell it what position you want it to turn to, and it'll go there. This is part of what makes servos so useful—there's not a lot of hoops to jump through to use them, even if you're using more than one at a time.

PART 3

LIGHT AND COLOR

CHAPTER 9

INTRO TO INDIVIDUALLY ADDRESSABLE LED STRIPS

———

Tools needed:

- Laptop computer (1)
- USB A to B cable (1)
- Wire cutters/strippers (1)

Parts needed:

- Arduino UNO (1)
- Individually addressable LED strip (any size or LED density will work)
- 22-gauge solid-core copper wire
- Electrical tape

Individually addressable LED strips are some of my favorite pieces of electronic hardware. Although they're fairly simple to use, they can produce incredible multicolored light displays and can be easily modified to suit many different kinds of projects and art pieces. In this chapter, we're going to learn about what individually addressable LED strips are, how they work, what they can do, and how to use them to create elaborate animated light displays for your art.

WHAT ARE INDIVIDUALLY ADDRESSABLE LED STRIPS?

LED strips are essentially very long, thin, and flexible circuit boards with evenly spaced LEDs mounted on them. There are two major types of LED strips. The more basic type has a number of LEDs on it that light up a specific color when powered on. These are commonly used for household decoration and are as simple as powering them on. However, these LED strips are completely static and will glow one color forever.

Some other types can let you change the color of the entire strip. This is accomplished by using **RGB LEDs**, which can be set to glow in any RGB color instead of single-color LEDs.

But the kind of LED strip we're going to be concerning ourselves within this book is the most dynamic and flexible type of LED strip there is—the **individually addressable LED strip**.

By adding a tiny silicon chip alongside every RGB LED in an LED strip, it becomes possible for each individual LED in an individually addressable LED strip to remember what color it's supposed to be. This means that a microcontroller such as an Arduino can *individually address* each LED on the strip and tell each one to be a different color at a different point in time.

This makes it possible to create visually stunning animated patterns of light using individually addressable LED strips. And as it happens, writing the code to make them do just that is surprisingly easy with the right tools. Plus, it's very easy to cut LED strips to the exact length that they need to be. That makes them a perfect candidate for any art project that involves lighting.

For instance, in this set design for a college production of the musical *Spring Awakening*, production designer Mellie Katakalos and lighting designer Will Lowry used LED strips to line the back wall of the set, creating a striking geometric pattern that both looked stunning and could be paired with the lighting design to enhance the emotional impact of scenes.[4] Just the LED strips on their own, though, are capable of telling an emotional story, which is what gives them so much power as a tool for art.

> Note: In this book, we'll be referring to individually addressable LED strips as just "LED Strips" for short.

PURCHASING AN LED STRIP

The NeoPixel is a model of individually addressable LED strip sold by Adafruit, an electronics manufacturer based in Brooklyn, New York. NeoPixels are high-quality strips with a lot of documentation, and Adafruit even sells a lot of other geometries of individually addressable NeoPixel products, such as LED rings and matrixes. However, they can be pricey, so it's worth considering strips made by other brands as well.

A number of manufacturers sell various types of WS2812B individually addressable LED strips. This is the type I recommend using with the projects in this book. These strips come in varying lengths, and strips that are the same length can also vary in density. Higher-density LED strips have more LEDs per inch and are typically pricier. The material connecting the LEDs in most strips are either white or black colored and are sometimes sold with silicone tubes to protect them. All of these variants make more sense for some projects than others, but none are inherently better or worse.

In the images in this book, the LED strip used is a 5-meter long white strip with a silicone sleeve and a density of 30 LEDs per meter, meaning it has 150 LEDs total. This is one of the lower densities of LED strip commonly manufactured.

---

4   Will Lowry and Melpomene Katakalos, *Spring Awakening*, 2019, wood and LED light strips, Diamond Theater, Zoellner Arts Center, Lehigh University, Bethlehem, Pennsylvania.

PLAYING WITH LED STRIPS

So, you've got your hands on a shiny new individually addressable LED strip, but before we get into the nitty-gritty of getting it to light up however you want it to, why not have some fun with it? In this project, we're going to hook one up to your Arduino and see what it can do.

1. Before we start, you need to download something called a code library. **Libraries** are collections of code files that make it easier to perform different programming tasks. The library we'll be using was developed by Adafruit for their NeoPixel product line but is perfectly compatible with similar strips from other brands.

   – You can download and install libraries either manually from the internet or via the Arduino IDE's library manager. To access the library manager, go to Tools > Manage Libraries in the menu bar.

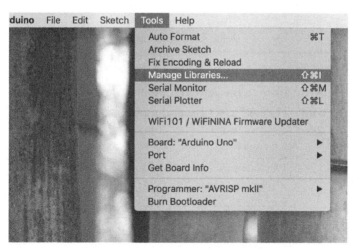

1. The library manager window as shown below should then open.

1. Once you've opened the library manager, click the search bar in the top right corner, type in "adafruit neopixel," and press enter/return. You should get search results that look like the following.

1. Scroll down to the third option, the one with only "Adafruit NeoPixel" as a title, and mouse over it.

1. Now click the "Install" button at the bottom left corner of the search result. This will automatically install the library on your computer. Once the installation is done, you can safely exit the library manager.

   - You can verify that the library has been installed by going to Sketch > Include Library and checking to see if "Adafruit NeoPixel" appears as an option. Your list of installed libraries will likely look different than the one below, and it's possible that the Adafruit NeoPixel library will be in a different spot on your list.

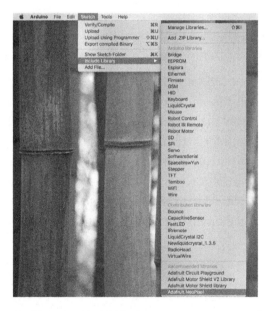

If the Adafruit NeoPixel library appears on your list, the installation was successful.

1. Before we can test out your LED strip, we must, of course, connect your LED strip to the Arduino. The actual steps you may need to complete to get your LED strip to connect

well might vary depending on what LED strips you have. The strip used in this chapter is a generic WS2812B LED strip—if yours is different, that's okay. All that's really important is that you can connect the black wire from your LED strip to one of the GND pins on your Arduino, the red wire to the +5V pin, and the green wire to pin 6. As long as all three of those connections are stable, you should be fine.

1. First, take a close look at one end of your LED strip.

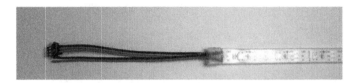

   – Your LED strip has two ends, but the Arduino can only transmit information in one direction. The direction of the arrows on the strip indicates the direction that information will travel through it—we have to use the side with the arrow pointing *away* from the connector wires because we want the information to travel from the Arduino into the connector wires and then through the entire strip.

   – Most LED strips have male and female connectors at the end to make it easy to connect them to other strips to make even longer super-strips. The problem is, this also makes it harder to connect the strip to the Arduino.

How to Create Stunning Multimedia Art with Electronics

- There are two main ways to deal with this issue. The first is to simply cut off the connector, strip the wires, and plug those into the Arduino. A less brute-force solution, and the one I personally prefer, requires one of these bad boys.

- This is a male connector that attaches to the female connector and comes with wires ready to be stripped.

2. Prepare your LED strip wires for connection to the Arduino. One option is to simply connect the male connector, strip the ends of the wires, and jam them into the Arduino pins. The trouble with this is that the wires in this cable are likely to be **stranded wires**, as opposed to the solid-core wires you've been using thus far. That means that instead of being one solid piece of copper coated in insulation, these wires are actually bundles of many different, smaller wires.

   - Stranded wires are useful for a number of reasons, one being that they are more flexible than stiff solid-core wire. The trouble with them is that it is often difficult to stick them into Arduino and breadboard pins. You can do it, of course, and you're welcome to try, but if you try uploading code to control the LED strips to the Arduino and it doesn't work, insufficient contact between the stranded wires and the pins might be at fault. If you do try to connect the stranded wire directly to the Arduino pins, it helps to twist all the strands for each wire together to keep them stiff and straight.

– If you can't get them to connect well, a great solution is to attach them to short segments of solid-core wire. If you're using this method:

3. Cut and strip both ends of three short solid-core wires.

– Cross the ends of the wire over each other, cross them, and twist until the wires don't come apart easily.

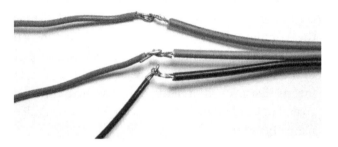

– Wrap the exposed copper in electrical tape to make sure that they don't accidentally cross and cause a short circuit.

4. Once all your preparation is done, connect the red wire to +5V, the black wire to one of the GND pins, and the green

wire to digital pin 6. The black and red wires are used to power the LEDs, and the green wire is used to transmit data from the Arduino to the LED strip.

5. Now that you're all wired up, it's time to run a test to make sure your LED works.

   – <numbered1>We aren't going to be writing any code of our own in this section. Instead, we're going to test your LED strip using a prewritten example code. Most libraries come with completed example code that you can access from the Arduino IDE's drop-down menus. These are very useful as references when writing your own code and also very useful for testing recently bought components to make sure they work before writing a bunch of code for them.

   – To access the example code we're going to use to test your LED strip, open File > Examples > Adafruit NeoPixel > strandtest.

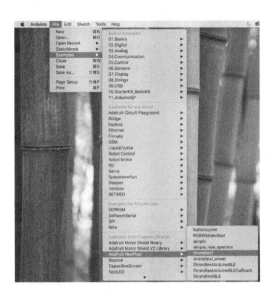

– This will open up an example code called "strand-test." It should look something like this:

- This example sketch is very long and introduces a lot of new things that we aren't going to talk about yet, so not all of it is reprinted here. For now, don't worry about trying to understand it.

6. Before we upload this sketch to the Arduino, we should make one little change, just to make sure you get the full effect of your LED strip's power. The strandtest sketch assumes that your LED strip has an LED count of 60, meaning that there are sixty LEDs on your strip. If you have more than this many LEDs, the sketch will still run but will only illuminate the first sixty LEDs on the strip and leave the others dark. To see the maximum effect of the code, it's worth making sure you know how many LEDs are on your strip.

   - When you bought your LED strip, the packaging or store page should have indicated the length and LED density of the strip. To get the number of LEDs on your LED strip, simply multiply these two numbers together. For instance, the LED strip shown in this section's images is five meters long and has an LED density of 30 LEDs per meter. Five times thirty is 150, so I have 150 LEDs on my LED strip.

   - If your LED strip has been cut or is an unusual size, another option is to simply count all of them by hand. This will also work fine, although it can be tedious for large strips.

   - Once you know the total number of LEDs on your LED strip, find this line near the top of the strandtest code:

```
#define LED _ COUNT 60
```

- Now, change the number sixty to the number of LEDs on your strip.

7. Plug your Arduino into your computer and upload this modified example code. You can save the file as your own code if you want, but there's no need to.

If everything is working properly, The LED should begin doing things like this.

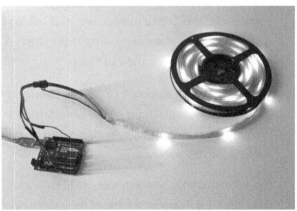

How to Create Stunning Multimedia Art with Electronics

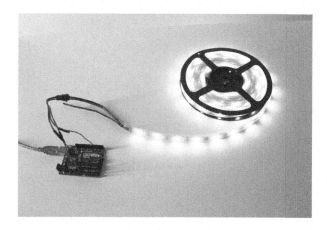

This is the power of individually addressable LED strips: they can create incredibly elaborate animated patterns of multi-colored lights. Beyond this, you can attach them together to make them even longer and can run several of them next to each other to make a sort of light matrix.

This example uses only four prewritten functions to control all of the different color animations the strip displays. One of them goes down the entire length of the LED strip and lights every LED up the same color one by one. Another simulates a flashing theater marquee light chase effect by turning every other LED on and off over and over again. The third makes every pixel cycle through a rainbow of colors, giving the entire strip a stunning animated rainbow pattern. The fourth is a combination of the last two, simulating a flashing theater marquee using rainbow colors.

This example code is hypnotic to watch and provides a great example of the massive flexibility of LED strips. In the next section, we're going to start writing our own sketches so that we can control them ourselves.

CHAPTER 10

PROGRAMMING LED STRIPS

———

Tools needed:

- Laptop computer (1)
- USB A to B cable (1)
- Wire cutters/strippers (1)

Parts needed:

- Arduino UNO (1)
- Individually addressable LED strip (any size or LED density will work)
- 22-gauge solid-core copper wire
- Electrical tape

Now that you've seen an LED strip in action, it's time to start learning how to program them yourself.

For our first sketch, we're going to make our own version of the function from the example sketch that lights up every LED on the strip one by one. In the following sketches, we're going to build on our first code and add more and more new functions that you can use to work with LED strips.

1. COLOR WIPE

Connect the LED strip as you did in the previous chapter, with the red wire connected to +5V, the black wire connected to GND, and the green wire connected to pin 6. Then open a new sketch in the Arduino IDE, type out the following code, and upload it.

```
// LED Strip Programming 1

#include <Adafruit_NeoPixel.h>

const int STRIP_PIN = 6; // pin connected to green wire of LED strip
const int LED_COUNT = 150; // number of LEDs on your strip (adjust if necessary)

// declare new LED strip named "strip"
Adafruit_NeoPixel strip(LED_COUNT, STRIP_PIN, NEO_GRB + NEO_KHZ800);

void setup() {
  strip.begin(); // initialize strip
  strip.show(); // turn off all LEDs on strip
  strip.setBrightness(50); // set brightness level to 50 out of 255
}

void loop() {
  wipe();
}

void wipe() { // turns on every LED in sequence
  int wait = 100; // number of milliseconds to wait after lighting LED

  for (int i = 0; i < strip.numPixels(); i++) {
    strip.setPixelColor(i, 255, 0, 0);
    strip.show(); // display changes made to LED settings
    delay(wait);
  }
}
```

If everything is working properly, every LED on the strip should turn red one by one, starting at the first LED, "wiping" a single color across the entire strip.

How to Create Stunning Multimedia Art with Electronics

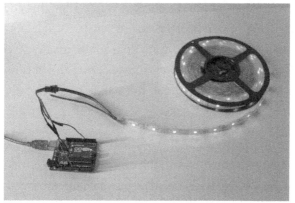

Let's look more closely at the code and see if we can discern what new tools this sketch gives us to work with LED strips.

Starting at the top of the sketch and moving down, we first encounter the following line of code:

```
#include <Adafruit _ NeoPixel.h>
```

#include is a syntactical term used in C++ and Arduino programming to "include" libraries, i.e., add their functionality to a sketch. After #include is the library is included, the Adafruit Neopixel library. I asked you to type this code in yourself, but in practice, the easiest way to include libraries is actually to have the Arduino do it automatically by going to Sketch > Include Library and selecting the library you want to include. This will tell the IDE to automatically add the #include line to the sketch.

Now that the functionality of the library has been added, we set up two constant variables to store some information about the strip for later use, namely, which pin the green wire of the strip is connected to and how many LEDs are on it.

```
const int STRIP _ PIN = 6; // pin connected
to green wire of LED strip
```

```
const int LED _ COUNT = 150; // number of
LEDs on your strip (adjust if necessary)
```

You can change these values if you choose to connect the green wire to another pin or if your LED strip has more or less than 150 LEDs.

And now, for our last piece of code before setup(), we have something entirely new:

```
// declare new LED strip named "strip"

Adafruit_NeoPixel strip(LED_COUNT,
STRIP_PIN, NEO_GRB + NEO_KHZ800);
```

This is our first foray into something called object-oriented programming.

There are several major ways that programmers typically organize code. The one we've been using so far is **functional programming**, which emphasizes the use of functions to work with data. But another common way is called **object-oriented programming**.

In simple terms, object-oriented programming is a method of writing code that focuses on organizing data into self-contained "objects." **Objects** are essentially little bundles of code that can use their own functions and store data that relates to the object.

For instance, if you were going to try to program a virtual car, you might create a "car" object. This "car" object would have a name, such as "blue car." It might have certain properties that you would store inside it, such as the color of the car and the maximum speed of the car. It might have certain functions that represent actions it could perform, such as "drive," "brake," and "roll down windows." This way, all the information about the car is stored in the "car" object, and other parts of the code could be written to interact with it.

The Adafruit NeoPixel library gives us the ability to create LED strip objects. In these LED strip objects, we can store information about our LED strip, such as the number of LEDs on the strip and the pin that the strip is connected to. The strip object has certain functions it can use to turn LEDs on the real-life strip on and off, and to change their color.

Let's take another look at the last line of code before setup().

```
Adafruit _ NeoPixel  strip(LED _ COUNT,
STRIP _ PIN, NEO _ GRB + NEO _ KHZ800);
```

This line of code is something called a **constructor**, which is a special kind of function in object-oriented programming that creates a new instance of an object. In a constructor, you put in all the initial information about the object that it needs in order to do its job. Objects, like variables, have a type that specifies what kind of object it is. The Adafruit NeoPixel library adds a new object type called Adafruit_NeoPixel.

This line of code creates a new Adafruit_NeoPixel object called strip. To create the object, its constructor requires three pieces of information: the number of LEDs on the strip, the Arduino pin connected to the data wire of the LED strip, and the color settings of the LED strip.

Here, we use the LED_COUNT and STRIP_PIN variables we just stored the appropriate information in to pass the appropriate specs of our LED strip to the object constructor. The last argument passed to the constructor, NEO_GRB + NEO_KHZ800, are color settings that represent how the Arduino needs to communicate with the LED strip for it to work. In most cases, using these exact parameters will work, but if you tell the LED strip to light up one color and it lights up a completely different one instead, try switching NEO_GRB to NEO_RGB—some strips use that setting instead.

Now we have an object called strip that we can use to control the LED strip! There's a little bookkeeping we have to do before we can get to the fun parts of using it, however.

```
void setup() {

strip.begin(); // initialize strip

strip.show(); // turn off all LEDs on strip

strip.setBrightness(50); // set brightness
level to 50 out of 255

}
```

In setup(), we jump straight into the deep end. The three lines of code between the brackets each use a different one of strip's functions. These sort of functions that "belong" to an object that the object can perform are called **methods**.

The first method is **strip.begin()**. This method has no parameters and serves only to initialize the LED strip. You need to use strip.begin() in your sketch before you can use any of strip's other methods. In this way, it works much like Serial.begin().

The second method is **strip.show()**. This method also has no parameters and is a very important one. When the Arduino runs strip.show(), strip will check its data to see which LEDs you've told it to set to which color, then turn all of them on at once. One interesting side effect of this is that before you actually tell it which LEDs should be which color, the object will assume all of them are supposed to be turned off. This means that calling strip.show() before you've told the strip to turn any of the LEDs on makes it turn all of the LEDs off.

This might seem useless—what's the point of turning all the LEDs off if you haven't turned any of them on yet?—but it can actually be important. See, as long as the LED strip is connected to power, it will remember which LEDs are supposed to be which color, so if you reset the sketch, all the LEDs from the last time you ran the sketch will remain on. This can make the execution of some sketches look different, so it's good practice to include this in the setup() of every sketch where you use LED strips.

The third method is **strip.setBrightness()**. This sketch has one parameter: a brightness level between 0 and 255. This tells the Arduino how much power to output to the strip and thus how bright the strip is. In general, try to use the lowest brightness you can use while still being able to see the LEDs glow. If you're working with several LED strips chained together, their power usage can be quite high, and you may not be able to power them all at a high brightness. A brightness level of fifty is usually satisfactory, and we'll be using it for all our projects in this book.

Okay, that's all the setup we need to do to be able to use an LED strip! Now let's move on to the part of the code that actually makes the LEDs do cool stuff.

This time, the loop() of this sketch is actually the simplest part of the code. It simply calls a user-defined function named wipe() over and over again.

```
void loop() {

wipe();

}
```

The wipe() function is the heart of this code and contains all the code that actually creates the animated effect of the LEDs.

```
void wipe() { // turns on every LED in
sequence

int wait = 100; // number of milliseconds
to wait after lighting LED

for (int i = 0; i < strip.numPixels();
i++) {

strip.setPixelColor(i, 255, 0, 0);

strip.show(); // display changes made to
LED settings

delay(wait);

}

}
```

Luckily for us, there are only really two parts of this function that are new. It starts by creating a variable called wait to store the number of milliseconds to pause between lighting up each new LED—nothing we haven't seen before.

The next part, however, is completely new.

```
for (int i = 0; i < strip.numPixels();
i++) {
```

```
strip.setPixelColor(i, 255, 0, 0);
```

```
strip.show(); // display changes made to
LED settings
```

```
delay(wait);
```

```
}
```

To understand this important piece of code, we need to learn about how things called "for loops" work.

```
For Loops
```

For loops are one of the three types of loops you can write in C++. A **loop** is a programming structure that encloses a block of code and runs it multiple times, just like the loop() function runs its contents over and over again until the Arduino is turned off.

For loops are a kind of loop designed to run a set number of times. Other kinds of loops can theoretically loop forever, but for loops are used when you know how many times you want the code inside to be executed. They are also extremely useful for running the same code over and over again *a little bit differently every time.*

Most important right now is that for loops are powerful tools for controlling LED strips. In the next few sections, we're going to see them again and again, so it's good to get familiar with them now.

A basic for loop looks something like this:

```
for (int i = 0; i < 3; i++) {

// code to loop

}
```

For loops require three pieces of information to run.

- An *index variable* that keeps track of how many times the loop has run.
  - A *condition* that tells the loop what condition must be true for it to run.
  - An *increment* that changes the value of the index variable after every iteration of the loop.

Each of these pieces of information is passed to the for loop one after the other in the parentheses after the word "for" like so:

```
(index variable; condition; increment) {

// code to loop

}
```

Note: For loops require you to separate this information with semicolons instead of with commas like you might when passing arguments to a function. If you accidentally use commas instead, the loop won't work.

Let's take another look at our "basic for loop" example to see how the information required by the for loop controls its performance. This time, though, let's add something in between the brackets for the code to actually do.

```
for (int i = 0; i < 3; i++) {

Serial.println(i); // print current value
of i to serial monitor

}
```

This will help give us some feedback on what's actually going on in the for loop while it's running.

Before the first semicolon in the parentheses, we *declare an index variable* for the for loop to use.

```
int i = 0
```

This creates a new integer variable called i (short for **index**, which means the number that keeps track of how the loop has run) and sets its initial value to 0. The index variable's initial value does not have to be zero, but the variable must be given an initial value to work.

Next up is the *condition*.

```
i < 3
```

As long as this condition is *true*, the for loop will continue to run. In this case, that means that as long as the value of the index variable "i" is less than 3, the loop will run.

The last piece of the puzzle comes after the second semicolon. This is the *increment*.

```
i++
```

After all of the code inside the for loop's brackets has been run, it will perform the action specified here to the index variable. "i++" is programming shorthand for "i = i + 1," meaning that the value of i will be increased by 1 after every time the loop is run.

Let's look at all of this at the same time now.

```
for (int i = 0; i < 3; i++) {

Serial.println(i); // print current value
of i to serial monitor

}
```

- The loop first creates a new variable called i and sets its value to 0.
- Cycle 1:
  - The for loop then checks to see if i is less than 3. Because i is equal to 0 and 0 is less than 3, the condition is true, and the contents of the loop run.
  - Serial.println(i) is run, printing the value 0 to the serial monitor.
  - i++ is run, increasing the value of i by 1. The value of i is now 1.

- Cycle 2:
  - The for loop then checks to see if i is less than 3. Because i is equal to 1 and 1 is less than 3, the condition is true, and the contents of the loop run.
  - Serial.println(i) is run, printing the value 1 to the serial monitor.
  - i++ is run, increasing the value of i by 1. The value of i is now 2.

- Cycle 3:
  - The for loop then checks to see if i is less than 3. Because i is equal to 2 and 2 is less than 3, the condition is true, and the contents of the loop run.
  - Serial.println(i) is run, printing the value 2 to the serial monitor.
  - i++ is run, increasing the value of i by 1. The value of i is now 3.

- Cycle 4:
  - The for loop then checks to see if i is less than 3. **Because i is equal to 3 and 3 is not less than 3, the condition is false, and the contents of the loop do not run.**

- The loop terminates, and the Arduino moves on to running the code after the loop.

After the for loop has run to completion, the serial monitor's output will look like this.

0
1
2

Thus, by starting the index variable at 0 and telling the for loop to terminate when i > 3, the loop will run exactly three times (although it won't actually display the numbers 1, 2, and 3).

1. COLOR WIPE, CONT.

Now that we know what a basic for loop looks like, we should be able to understand the for loop in this sketch.

```
for (int i = 0; i < strip.numPixels();
i++) {

strip.setPixelColor(i, 255, 0, 0);

strip.show(); // display changes made to
LED settings

delay(wait);

}
```

Let's ignore the contents of the for loop for now and just look at the loop definition.

```
for (int i = 0; i < strip.numPixels();
i++) {

// cool LED strip stuff

}
```

The index variable declaration and the increment are both exactly the same as in the example earlier, but the condition is a bit different. We're still telling the for loop to run until the value of i is less than another value, but in the place of a specific value, we have strip.numPixels().

strip.numPixels() is the next LED strip method for us to look at today. This method takes no arguments and simply returns the number of LEDs on the strip represented by the strip object.

What this means is that the for loop will run one time for every single LED on the LED strip. This is a very simple way to use for loops to write a small amount of code and apply it separately to hundreds or even thousands of LEDs and is a technique we will be using in almost every sketch we will write.

This technique begs an obvious question: why not just use a constant value? We know we have 150 LEDs on our strip—couldn't I just use the number 150 instead?

The answer is: yes! Of course, you can. But the beauty of this method is that it lets us program a specific method and then scale it to any length of LED strip. If you plugged another LED strip into the end of this one, all you would have to do to extend the wipe animation across both strips is to change the line const int LED_COUNT = 150 at the start of the code to const int LED_COUNT = 300 and the animation would simply continue until it reached the end of the second strip as well. You could also lower the value of LED_COUNT if you only wanted the wipe to go partway down the length of the strip.

We're going to be using adaptive programming techniques like this for the rest of our sketches as well for the same reason.

Now let's consider the code inside the loop—in other words, the code that will run for each individual LED on the entire length of the strip.

```
for (int i = 0; i < strip.numPixels();
i++) {

strip.setPixelColor(i, 255, 0, 0);

strip.show(); // display changes made to
LED settings

delay(wait);

}
```

First we start with our last new LED strip object method of this sketch. **strip.setPixelColor()** is the method responsible for actually setting the color of LEDs on the strip.

strip.setPixelColor() has a few different sets of acceptable parameters, but in this sketch, the ones we're using are

```
strip.setPixelColor(ledNumber, red, green,
blue)
```

where ledNumber is an integer value representing which LED you're setting the color of and red, green, and blue are integer values between 0 and 255 that represent the respective levels of red, blue, and green in the color you'd like the LED to be.

Every LED on your LED strip has a certain number representing its position relative to the Arduino connected to it. The very first LED connected to the Arduino is LED #0. The one that is one step farther away from the Arduino is LED #1. The one after that is #2, so on and so forth until the end of the strip. Just like our for loop index starts at 0, the first LED on your strip is #0. On a strip with 150 LEDs, then the LED furthest away from the Arduino must be LED #149. So, if you use strip.setPixelColor to set the color of pixel 3, it will actually set the color of the fourth LED on the strip if you start counting from the closest LED to the Arduino.

In this sketch, the value of ledNumber is set to i, a number that changes every time the loop is run. On the first iteration of the loop, i will equal 0, setting the color of the first LED. The next time, it will equal 1, setting the color of the second LED. This will continue until every LED on the strip has been assigned a color.

The red, green, and blue values all kind of go together. This part works much like the way an RGB color picker in a paint application might. Each of the LEDs on the strip is an RGB LED, meaning you can choose how much red, green, and blue light the LED should output, allowing you to mix the three to create secondary and primary colors.

There are a few differences between how color might work on your computer, on an LED strip, and using a physical medium like paint, however. The first major difference is that RGB LEDs can't make the color black. On a computer, you would do this by setting each of the values of red, green, and blue to 0. On an LED strip, setting red, green, and blue to 0 will simply turn them off. This is the default setting of each LED on the strip when it is first supplied with power, although they will not reset to this value if the sketch resets.

Conversely, setting the values of red, green, and blue to 255 will make something akin to white light. It won't be perfectly white since it's just your eye's visual approximation of the combination of red, green, and blue.

Note: If you need your LEDs to shine a pure white color, you should use an RGBW LED strip, which adds a white diode to each RGB LED to really make the white light pop. For now, though, we're going to stick with RGB LEDs.

Note that additive color theory (as is used in lighting) and subtractive color theory (as is used in painting) have different rules. The most obvious difference between the two is that mixing red, green, and blue light will make a bright white-ish color, while mixing red, green, and blue paint together will create a dark, muddled mess. Similarly, trying to combine red, green, and blue light to create colors can sometimes have results that seem a little off compared to what you might expect from making the same combinations with paint. In this way, using LED strips has much more in common with using something like stage lighting than it does with other physical media.

In this sketch, red is set to 255 (full power) while green and blue are both set to 0 (off). This sets each LED to the color red. Feel free to play around with the values of red, green, and blue and reupload the sketch to see what other colors you can make the strip.

The last thing to keep in mind about strip.setPixelColor() is that it doesn't actually turn LEDs on or off. All it does is update the color value that each LED is supposed to be set to, whether it's all the way off, all the way on, or somewhere in between. The function that actually pushes this information to the LED strip is strip.show(), which is incidentally the function immediately following strip.setPixelColor() in this sketch.

```
for (int i = 0; i < strip.numPixels();
i++) {
```

```
strip.setPixelColor(i, 255, 0, 0);
```

```
strip.show(); // display changes made to
LED settings
```

```
delay(wait);
```

```
}
```

As seen here, we first update the color value of whichever LED corresponds to the current cycle of the for loop using strip.setPixelColor(), then output that change to the strip using strip.show(). Because the only color value that gets changed every time is the new one that's being lit up, strip.show() doesn't change any of the LEDs that have already been lit up, instead just lighting up the newest one every cycle through the for loop.

Finally, we add a short delay for the length of the wait variable declared before the for loop. This keeps the Arduino from turning on the LEDs so fast we can't see the animation—if you remove this delay function, the whole strip will light up in less than a second. And if you can barely even see the effect of the animation, what's the point?

The for loop turns every LED on the strip red one by one until it eventually reaches the end. After that, the wipe() function will run again and again since it's in the loop() statement, but because all the LEDs are already red, setting them all to red again does nothing. In our next sketch, we're going to add another function to our code that lets the strip repeat the animation over and over again.

Congratulations! You've already finished programming a complex LED strip animation. From here on out, we're going to work on new animations by building on this existing code only a few steps at a time.

2. ERASE ALL

Now that we've learned how to turn LEDs on, we're going to build on our previous sketch to write code that turns LEDs off—to be precise, every LED on the strip instantaneously.

Upload the following sketch to your Arduino.

```
// LED Strip Programming 2

#include <Adafruit_NeoPixel.h>

const int STRIP_PIN = 6; // pin connected to green wire of LED strip
const int LED_COUNT = 150; // number of LEDs on your strip (adjust if necessary)

// declare new LED strip named "strip"
Adafruit_NeoPixel strip(LED_COUNT, STRIP_PIN, NEO_GRB + NEO_KHZ800);

void setup() {
  strip.begin(); // initialize strip
  strip.show(); // turn off all LEDs on strip
  strip.setBrightness(50); // set brightness level to 50 out of 255
}

void loop() {
  wipe();
  delay(3000);
  eraseAll();
}


void wipe() { // turns on every LED in sequence
  int wait = 100; // number of milliseconds to wait after lighting LED

  for (int i = 0; i < strip.numPixels(); i++) {
    strip.setPixelColor(i, 255, 0, 0);
    strip.show(); // display changes made to LED settings
    delay(wait);
  }
}

void eraseAll() { // turns off all LEDs instantly
  for (int i = 0; i < strip.numPixels(); i++) {
    strip.setPixelColor(i, 0, 0, 0);
  }
  strip.show(); // display changes made to LED settings (all LEDs are off now)
}
```

If it works, your LED strip should wipe the color red across the entire strip as before and wait for three seconds. Then all the LEDs will turn off and the loop animation will start again. Rinse and repeat.

The LED strip begins the wipe as normal.

When the entire strip has finished lighting up...

The strip goes dark after three seconds and begins the process again.

The only changes between this sketch and the previous one are in the loop() and at the end, where a new function called eraseAll() is defined.

Let's glance at loop() real quick before we talk about how eraseAll() works.

```
void loop() {

wipe();

delay(3000);

eraseAll();

}
```

Just like in our last sketch, we call the wipe() function, which runs a full wipe animation along the entire length of the LED strip. However, now there are two functions that run afterward. First, as soon as the animation finishes, delay(3000) makes the Arduino wait for three seconds before doing anything. Afterward, eraseAll() is called, and then the loop repeats and runs the wipe() animation again.

eraseAll() is a function that, simply put, sets the color of every LED on the strip to black (AKA off) instantly. This means that now we can actually see wipe() happening more than once, whereas in the last sketch, wipe() would do its job over and over again, but since the LEDs were never told to turn off, you couldn't tell after the first loop.

Taking a look at the function definition for eraseAll(), you might notice it looks very similar to wipe().

```
void eraseAll() { // turns off all LEDs
instantly

for (int i = 0; i < strip.numPixels();
i++) {

strip.setPixelColor(i, 0, 0, 0);

}

strip.show(); // display changes made to
LED settings (all LEDs are off now)

}
```

The main difference between how eraseAll() works and how wipe() works is that we don't need as many bells and whistles for eraseAll(). eraseAll(), in fact, is almost exactly the same as wipe(), except that now we're using a for loop to update the color of every LED to the RGB value (0, 0, 0), which is black (off). But since this time we don't need to animate it, and in fact don't want the viewer to see it happening, we want the wipe to happen as quickly as possible.

For this reason, we can remove the wait variable declaration you see in wipe(), remove the delay() entirely, and move strip. show() *outside of the for loop* so it only runs one time, after the color of every LED has already been updated to black. Even though it does take a small amount of time to update every LED on the strip (a few milliseconds per LED), this will maximize the speed at which the Arduino can change the color value of every LED and then allow it to update the entire strip instantaneously.

This function is useful for many different LED animations, so we're going to be using it often in our next few sketches.

3. WIPE WITH PARAMETERS

It's time to take things up a notch and make our original wipe() method a lot more flexible. Right now, we've gotten it to work with the color red, but what if we want to do wipes in multiple different colors without having to write an entirely new function? This time, we're going to enhance the function with parameters to allow us to change how it operates throughout the program.

Upload the following code to your Arduino.

```
LED_Strip_Wipe_Parameters
// LED Strip Programming 3

#include <Adafruit_NeoPixel.h>

const int STRIP_PIN = 6; // pin connected to green wire of LED strip
const int LED_COUNT = 150; // number of LEDs on your strip (adjust if necessary)

// declare new LED strip named "strip"
Adafruit_NeoPixel strip(LED_COUNT, STRIP_PIN, NEO_GRB + NEO_KHZ800);

void setup() {
  strip.begin(); // initialize strip
  strip.show(); // turn off all LEDs on strip
  strip.setBrightness(50); // set brightness level to 50 out of 255
}

void loop() {
  // red wipe
  wipe(50, 255, 0, 0);
  eraseAll();

  // green wipe
  wipe(100, 0, 255, 0);
  eraseAll();

  // blue wipe
  wipe(25, 0, 0, 255);
  eraseAll();
}

void wipe(int wait, int r, int g, int b) { // turns on every LED in sequence
  for (int i = 0; i < strip.numPixels(); i++) {
    strip.setPixelColor(i, r, g, b);
    strip.show(); // display changes made to LED settings
    delay(wait);
  }
}

void eraseAll() { // turns off all LEDs instantly
  for (int i = 0; i < strip.numPixels(); i++) {
    strip.setPixelColor(i, 0, 0, 0);
  }
  strip.show(); // display changes made to LED settings (all LEDs are off now)
}
```

```
10                                    Arduino Uno on /dev/cu.usbmodem14511
```

This time, the wipe animation will run three times before resetting. The first time, the LEDs in the wipe will turn red. The second time, they'll turn green, and the wipe will be slower. The third time, they'll turn blue, and the wipe will be a lot faster.

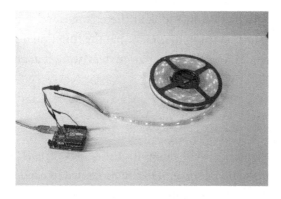

The LED strip wiping in red.

The LED strip wiping in green.

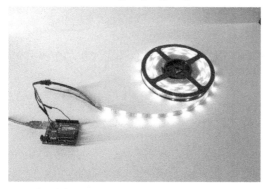

The LED strip wiping in blue.

Let's begin by taking a look at the changes we've made to wipe(). The first thing to note is that the function definition now includes four different parameters: wait, r, g, and b.

```
void wipe(int wait, int r, int g, int b) {
// turns on every LED in sequence
```

r, g, and b are the RGB values for the color that each LED in the wipe should be set to. wait functions just like it did in the old version of the function, except that now instead of being declared in the first line of the function with a fixed value, its value can vary depending on the first argument passed to the function.

The function as a whole doesn't work much differently than the original version.

```
void wipe(int wait, int r, int g, int b) {
// turns on every LED in sequence

for (int i = 0; i < strip.numPixels();
i++) {

strip.setPixelColor(i, r, g, b);

strip.show(); // display changes made to
LED settings

delay(wait);

}

}
```

The main difference between the two is that instead of using a fixed color value, now we just pass r, g, and b directly to the red, green, and blue parameters of strip.setPixelColor(). That means that the color each pixel gets set to now depends on what arguments are passed to the function when the function is called elsewhere in the sketch.

Likewise, although the number of milliseconds to delay() between lighting up each pixel is still equal to the value of wait, the value of wait is now dependent on the first argument passed to the function. Thus, giving wait larger values will increase the length of time it takes to wipe across the entire strip while giving it smaller values will decrease the length of time the wipe takes.

We need to look no further than the loop() to see how this is implemented in our sketch.

```
void loop() {

// red wipe

wipe(50, 255, 0, 0);

eraseAll();

/ green wipe

wipe(100, 0, 255, 0);

eraseAll();

// blue wipe
```

```
wipe(25, 0, 0, 255);
```

```
eraseAll();
```

```
}
```

This loop() is split into three separate wipe() animations, each one for a different color. After each wipe(), eraseAll()is called to reset the LED strip for the next wipe. (You could, however, remove the eraseAll() functions if you wanted each wipe to simply "paint over" the previous one without resetting first. This is also a cool effect, and I recommend trying it out.)

The first call of wipe() uses the following parameters.

```
wipe(50, 255, 0, 0);
```

This sets the value of wait in the function to 50, which is half the length of the delay this sketch had in earlier versions. As a result, the wipe animation completes nearly twice as fast as in the previous two sketches.

The next three values are the RGB values, setting the value of r to 255 and the values of g and b to 0. This makes the wipe color red.

The second wipe uses the values shown below:

```
wipe(100, 0, 255, 0);
```

wait is now 100, effectively doubling the time the wipe() takes compared to the last time. Now the RBG values are (0, 255, 0), making the wipe color green.

Last but not least, we have the final wipe() in the loop.

```
wipe(25, 0, 0, 255);
```

This one sets the value of wait to the smallest value yet, making the wipe quite fast. The RGB value is now (0, 0, 255), making the wipe color blue.

This is part of why it's useful to write LED strip animations and lighting patterns as functions. You've essentially managed to write an infinite number of different-looking versions of the same LED wipe with only a few lines of code, and with just a few more modifications, you could add even more variety to the style of the animation.

4. COLOR TOOLS

Now that we've worked on making some neat animations, it's time to learn about some additional tools the NeoPixel library gives us for working with colors.

Upload the following sketch to your Arduino. There might be a few things in this one that look a little foreign, but I promise I'll explain them in a moment.

```
LED_Strip_Color_Tools

// LED Strip Programming 4

#include <Adafruit_NeoPixel.h>

const int STRIP_PIN = 6; // pin connected to green wire of LED strip
const int LED_COUNT = 150; // number of LEDs on your strip (adjust if necessary)

// declare new LED strip named "strip"
Adafruit_NeoPixel strip(LED_COUNT, STRIP_PIN, NEO_GRB + NEO_KHZ800);

void setup() {
  strip.begin(); // initialize strip
  strip.show(); // turn off all LEDs on strip
  strip.setBrightness(50); // set brightness level to 50 out of 255
}

void loop() {
  uint32_t red = strip.Color(255, 0, 0);
  uint32_t green = strip.Color(0, 255, 0);
  uint32_t blue = strip.Color(0, 0, 255);

  // red wipe
  wipe(50, red);
  eraseAll();

  // green wipe
  wipe(100, green);
  eraseAll();

  // blue wipe
  wipe(25, blue);
  eraseAll();
}

void wipe(int wait, uint32_t color) { // turns on every LED in sequence
  for (int i = 0; i < strip.numPixels(); i++) {
    strip.setPixelColor(i, color);
    strip.show(); // display changes made to LED settings
    delay(wait);
  }
}

void eraseAll() { // turns off all LEDs instantly
  for (int i = 0; i < strip.numPixels(); i++) {
    strip.setPixelColor(i, 0, 0, 0);
  }
  strip.show(); // display changes made to LED settings (all LEDs are off now)
}
```

Arduino Uno on /dev/cu.usbmodem14511

This sketch should produce exactly the same final result as the previous sketch, with three different LED wipes in red, green, and blue. However, this time, we've programmed it a lot differently.

If you look closely, you'll notice that wipe() now only requires two parameters.

```
void wipe(int wait, uint32 _ t color) { //
turns on every LED in sequence
```

wait is the same as before, but what the heck is this new thing?

What this new version of the sketch is all about is *representing RGB colors using a single value.* To match that, the wipe() function has been rewritten to only take a single value that represents the entire color of the LED. To store all the color information in a single variable, however, we need to use a new data type.

The **uint32_t** data type is essentially a special version of an integer. It's not used very commonly in Arduino programming, but is typically the go-to data type for storing color values for use with LED strips. The "u" stands for "unsigned," meaning "doesn't have a positive or negative value." The "32_t" indicates that this kind of integer is made to store exactly 32 bits of data—no more, no less. All you really need to know about it is that this variable type is what we're going to be storing colors in while programming LED strips.

If we take a closer look at the wipe() function as a whole, we can see one more important difference from last time.

```
void wipe(int wait, uint32 _ t color) { //
turns on every LED in sequence
```
```
for (int i = 0; i < strip.numPixels();
i++) {
```
```
strip.setPixelColor(i, color);
```

```
strip.show(); // display changes made to
LED settings
```

```
delay(wait);
```

```
}
```

```
}
```

Did you catch it? It's this line:

```
strip.setPixelColor(i, color);
```

Remember how I mentioned that strip.setPixelColor() has a few different sets of acceptable parameters? Up until now, we've only been using the RGB parameters to set the colors of different pixels.

```
strip.setPixelColor(ledNumber, red, green,
blue)
```

But if you have the color you want to set the LED to in the form of a uint32_t value, you can also use this set of parameters to call the function:

```
strip.setPixelColor(ledNumber, color)
```

where color is a uint32_t value representing the color to change the LED to.

What's the advantage to doing it this way rather than just using RGB values everywhere? Well, there are several, but some of the most important are that it makes your code easier to read and that it makes it possible to store the values of colors you like in your program.

For a perfect example of this, we need look no further than the loop().

```
void loop() {

uint32_t red = strip.Color(255, 0, 0);

uint32_t green = strip.Color(0, 255, 0);

uint32_t blue = strip.Color(0, 0, 255);

// red wipe

wipe(50, red);

eraseAll();

// green wipe

wipe(100, green);

eraseAll();

// blue wipe

wipe(25, blue);

eraseAll();

}
```

This version of the loop() starts by actually storing the values of the colors we use for each of the wipes later.

```
uint32_t red = strip.Color(255, 0, 0);
```

```
uint32_t green = strip.Color(0, 255, 0);
```

```
uint32_t blue = strip.Color(0, 0, 255);
```

These three lines of code declare three variables of the type uint32_t called red, green, and blue and assigns them each a color value. How do we actually get the value of each of these colors, you ask? Well, the simplest way is to use an especially helpful method of the Adafruit_NeoPixel object type.

strip.Color() is a method that takes RGB values as arguments and returns a uint32_t value representing that RGB color. It doesn't actually make the strip do anything—it's purely a computational tool used to store RGB colors in a single value.

The parameters of strip.Color() are:

```
strip.Color(red, green, blue)
```

Where red, green, and blue are integer values between 0 and 255 that represent the respective levels of red, blue, and green in color. Note that the letter C in "Color" is capitalized.

That's fairly straightforward, right? Storing color values like this is especially useful when you're experimenting with different RGB value combinations to try to find one that really works for your piece.

Now, since we've stored the color values we want to use in this sketch, we're able to call the wipe() functions using them for the rest of the loop().

```
// red wipe

wipe(50, red);

eraseAll();

// green wipe

wipe(100, green);

eraseAll();

// blue wipe

wipe(25, blue);

eraseAll();
```

Notice how much clearer this code is now that we can actually read the color being used in each wipe instead of having to look at four different parameters, determine which three are the RGB values, and then figure out based on those three values what color it must be. That process would be even more difficult if we were using more complex RGB values— can you figure out what color (50, 200, 120) looks like in your head? Of course not.

Next, we're going to learn even more about the tools the NeoPixel library gives us to work with color, and in doing so, we're going to push the visual dazzle of your LED strip to the next level.

5. RAINBOW WIPE

The NeoPixel library includes a number of useful methods that we haven't talked about yet. One of these is called **strip. ColorHSV()**. The output of this method is just like strip. Color(), but instead of taking RGB values as inputs, it takes numbers that represent the hue, saturation, and value of the desired color.

A color's **hue** is essentially its place on the color spectrum. It determines whether a color is one of the primary colors or somewhere in between. **Saturation** is how intense the color is—bright apple-red would be a high-saturation color, whereas a pastel pink would be lower saturation. **Brightness** is how dark or bright a color is. If you took a black-and-white image of a bright color, it would appear closer to white, while a dark color might look more like black.

Because it grants you the ability to incrementally adjust the hue of your LEDs, the strip.ColorHSV() function is especially useful for writing code that transitions the LEDs on your strip between different colors on the color wheel. In this sketch, we'll be modifying our wipe() function to take advantage of this and create a rainbow effect.

Upload the following sketch to your Arduino and watch what your LED strip does.

```
LED_Strip_Rainbow_Wipe | Arduino 1.8.13

LED_Strip_Rainbow_Wipe

// LED Strip Programming 5

#include <Adafruit_NeoPixel.h>

const int STRIP_PIN = 6; // green wire of
const int LED_COUNT = 150; // number of LEDs on your strip (adjust if necessary)

// declare new LED strip named "strip"
Adafruit_NeoPixel strip(LED_COUNT, STRIP_PIN, NEO_GRB + NEO_KHZ800);

void setup() {
  strip.begin(); // initialize strip
  strip.show(); // turn off all LEDs on strip
  strip.setBrightness(50); // set brightness level to 50 out of 255
}

void loop() {
  rainbowWipe(100);
  delay(3000);
  eraseAll();
}

void rainbowWipe(int wait) { // turns on every LED in a rainbow
  long hue = 0; // stores hue value of current LED

  for (int i = 0; i < strip.numPixels(); i++) {
    // calculate RGB color value from hue and perform gamma correction on it
    uint32_t color = strip.gamma32(strip.ColorHSV(hue));

    strip.setPixelColor(i, color); // set color of LED

    // update hue value for next pixel
    hue = hue + (65536 / strip.numPixels());

    strip.show();
    delay(wait);
  }
}

void eraseAll() { // turns off all LEDs instantly
  for (int i = 0; i < strip.numPixels(); i++) {
    strip.setPixelColor(i, 0, 0, 0);
  }
  strip.show(); // display changes made to LED settings (all LEDs are off now)
}
```
```
1                                          Arduino Uno on /dev/cu.usbmodem14511
```

If all goes well, your LED strip should be lighting up one LED at a time just like before, except this time the color will slowly change along the length of the strip, going through the entire color spectrum until it reaches the end.

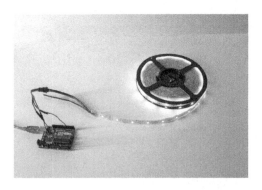

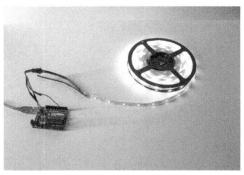

All the setup here is the same as before. Now, however, we're using a very different version of the wipe() function, so different that we've renamed it rainbowWipe().

```
void loop()  {

rainbowWipe(100);

delay(3000);

eraseAll();

}
```

rainbowWipe() is very similar to wipe(), but there are a few
key differences in how it works.

```
void rainbowWipe(int wait) { // turns on
every LED in a rainbow
```

```
long hue = 0; // stores hue value of current LED
```

```
for (int i = 0; i < strip.numPixels();
i++) {
```

```
// calculate RGB color value from hue and
perform gamma correction on it
```

```
uint32_t color = strip.gamma32(strip.
ColorHSV(hue));
```

```
strip.setPixelColor(i, color); // set color of LED
```

```
// update hue value for next pixel
```

```
hue = hue + (65536 / strip.numPixels());
```

```
  strip.show();
```

```
  delay(wait);
```

```
}
```

```
}
```

The first major difference is the declaration of a new variable called hue.

```
long hue = 0; // stores hue value of
current LED
```

hue is defined as a data type we haven't seen before. The **long** data type is basically a big integer. long variables can hold much, much bigger numbers than ints, but they take up a lot more space in the Arduino's memory, so it's best to only use them when you need to store or do math with values that are so large that the Arduino can't store them.

This variable is going to store the hue value that the next LED is going to be set to in the for loop.

Speaking of the for loop, we have one again here, set up in exactly the same way as it was in wipe(). The next lines, however, have some new stuff.

```
// calculate RGB color value from hue and
perform gamma correction on it
```
```
uint32 _ t color = strip.gamma32(strip.
ColorHSV(hue));
```

On the left side of the second line, we store a color value in a uint32_t variable called color. On the right side, we have two methods that will calculate the color value to store.

Let's start with **strip.ColorHSV()**. As mentioned earlier, this is a method that takes a hue, saturation, and value as parameters and returns a uint32_t color value. But here, you might notice that we're only using one parameter. Why is that?

That's because this method has two definitions. The first takes only one parameter—hue—and automatically sets the saturation and value to maximum.

```
strip.ColorHSV(hue)
```

The other takes all three parameters. This is useful for picking really specific colors.

```
strip.ColorHSV(hue, saturation, value)
```

saturation and value can be between 0 (low) and 255 (high). However, in the NeoPixel library, hue can be any value from 0 to 65,535. Actually, it can be even higher than that—the cycle will continue as the hue value increases above 65,535.

This is to give you a very high degree of precision in cycling through different colors, which is especially useful for creating rainbow effects. A hue value of 0 will produce the color red—cycling through every hue value until you reach 65,535 will produce every color on the color wheel until red is eventually reached again. This makes strip. ColorHSV()an invaluable tool for producing rainbow color effects.

Let's take a quick look at that last line of code again.

```
uint32_t color = strip.gamma32(strip.
ColorHSV(hue));
```

You might notice that strip.ColorHSV(hue) is actually *inside* the parentheses of strip.gamma32().

In this situation, putting strip.ColorHSV() inside strip. gamma32() means that whatever value strip.ColorHSV() returns will be passed to strip.gamma32() as an argument. That means that the final value assigned to color will be the value returned by strip.gamma32().

strip.gamma32() is the last new method for this sketch. It's essentially a conversion tool that takes a uint32_t color value as an input and outputs another uint32_t color value as an output.

You could omit this method from this sketch, and it would still run fine—the changes it makes are usually relatively minor. But why do we include it?

You see, LED strips use PWM (pulse-width-modulation) to control how much of each color (red, green, and blue) to shine to produce more specific colors. LED strips, being very precise machines, will do this correctly and perfectly. But you know what aren't very precise machines? Human eyes.

Sadly, human eyes were not made for the purpose of looking at pretty LEDs flash in rainbow colors. They were made for the purpose of keeping the human they were attached to from dying.

One of the evolutionary consequences of this is that human eyes are more sensitive to low levels of light and less sensitive to high levels of light. That means that they won't always perceive the literal colors being output by the LEDs correctly, especially due to the effect of PWM—for instance, if an LED was trying to produce purple by flashing blue 100 percent of the time and flashing red 50 percent of the time, your eyes would be oversensitive to the red and undersensitive to the blue. This will skew the perceived color of the LED for the viewer.

The solution to this is something called **gamma correction**, or altering colors so that they will be perceived correctly. That's the purpose of strip.gamma32()—it takes a color value as input, runs it through a formula to determine what it's supposed to look like to the viewer, what it will *actually* look like to the viewer, and then returns a new color value that compensates for your eyes and will actually look like it's supposed to in practice.

strip.gamma32() has one parameter:

```
strip.gamma32(originalColor);
```

where originalColor is the uint32_t color value to perform gamma correction on.

Now let's take this line of code all at once.

```
uint32 _ t color = strip.gamma32(strip.
ColorHSV(hue));
```

To summarize: This line creates a new uint32_t variable called color and assigns it a gamma-corrected color value based on the current value of hue, which represents a position on the color wheel.

The next line of code is one we've seen before: It sets the color of the next LED on the strip.

```
strip.setPixelColor(i, color); // set color
of LED
```

Now that we've assigned the color we calculated from the hue value to a pixel, we're going to want the pixel that comes after this to be a different color a little bit further around the color wheel. We can accomplish this by increasing the hue value after every time we set the color of a new LED.

But how much do we need to change the hue value by? Well, that depends. In this case, we want the entire "rainbow," which in this case means every color on the color wheel, to be present in a gradient across the entire length of the LED strip. But it's pretty unlikely that your LED strip has 65,536 LEDs on it, and the difference between each of those tens of thousands of hue values would be imperceptible anyway unless you could see every single one of them at the same time.

So instead, let's take the total number of possible hue values (65,536) and divide it by the number of LEDs on your strip. That will split the color wheel into even-sized ranges of hues. Then we can just add the size of each of these "ranges" to the value of hue for each new pixel. That way, the color of each new LED will slowly transition across the entire rainbow between the beginning and end of the strip.

The way we can execute this math is like so:

```
// update hue value for next pixel

hue = hue + (65536 / strip.numPixels());
```

This assigns hue a new value equal to its current value plus the total number of possible hues divided by the number of pixels on the strip. By using strip.numPixels() here, this code will work regardless of the length of the LED strip you're using.

Lastly, we show the changes made during this iteration of the loop and pause for a specified length of time before continuing.

```
strip.show();
```

```
delay(wait);
```

And there you have it! A fully functional rainbow wipe. Pretty neat, huh? Well, you ain't seen nothin' yet.

6. RAINBOW

This sketch demonstrates the full power of individually addressable LED strips. When you upload it, if everything's in order, every LED on the strip will independently cycle through the entire color spectrum. It should look like a rainbow flowing across your strip like water.

```
LED_Strip_Rainbow | Arduino 1.8.13

LED_Strip_Rainbow
// LED Strip Programming 6

#include <Adafruit_NeoPixel.h>

const int STRIP_PIN = 6; // green wire of
const int LED_COUNT = 150; // number of LEDs on your strip (adjust if necessary)

// declare new LED strip named "strip"
Adafruit_NeoPixel strip(LED_COUNT, STRIP_PIN, NEO_GRB + NEO_KHZ800);

void setup() {
  strip.begin(); // initialize strip
  strip.show(); // turn off all LEDs on strip
  strip.setBrightness(50); // set brightness level to 50 out of 255
}

void loop() {
  rainbow(150);
}


void rainbow(int wait) { // cycles every LED through the entire color spectrum
  // cycle hue of first pixel through entire spectrum in 256-unit intervals
  for (long firstPixelHue = 0; firstPixelHue < 65536; firstPixelHue += 256) {
    // set every LED on strip to a different color on the spectrum
    for (int i = 0; i < strip.numPixels(); i++) {
      // determine hue of current pixel being set by loop
      int hue = firstPixelHue + (i * (65536 / strip.numPixels()));

      // calculate RGB color value from hue and perform gamma correction on it
      uint32_t color = strip.gamma32(strip.ColorHSV(hue));

      strip.setPixelColor(i, color); // set color of LED
    }

    strip.show(); // show changes to colors
    delay(wait); // wait before moving on to next step in animation
  }
}
```

```
1                                    Arduino Uno on /dev/cu.usbmodem145201
```

If all goes well, your strip should look something like this over time.

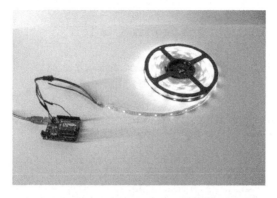

Pretty cool, eh?

Our story begins in the loop(), where our newest function is called.

```
void loop() {

rainbow(150);

}
```

This new function, rainbow(), has some similarities to rainbowWipe() but adds a layer of complexity.

```
void rainbow(int wait) { // cycles every
LED through the entire color spectrum
```

```
// cycle hue of first pixel through entire
spectrum in 256-unit intervals
```

```
for (long firstPixelHue = 0; firstPixelHue
< 65536; firstPixelHue += 256) {
```

```
// set every LED on strip to a different
color on the spectrum
```

```
for (int i = 0; i < strip.numPixels();
i++) {
```

```
// determine hue of current pixel being
set by loop
```

```
int hue = firstPixelHue + (i * (65536 /
strip.numPixels()));
```

```
// calculate RGB color value from hue and
perform gamma correction on it
```

```
uint32_t color = strip.gamma32(strip.
ColorHSV(hue));
```

```
strip.setPixelColor(i, color); // set color
of LED
```

```
}
```

```
strip.show(); // show changes to colors
```

```
delay(wait); // wait before moving on to
next step in animation
```

```
}
```

```
}
```

This function uses what are called "nested for loops." When something is **nested** in programming, it means that it's inside of something else—in this case, one for loop is inside of another. When one for loop is inside of another, the innermost loop will run completely for every single iteration of the outer loop. That means if you had an outer loop that ran ten times and an inner loop that ran 100 times, the contents of the inner loop would have run 1,000 times (10 * 100) by the time the outer loop was finished.

In this code, the innermost for loop works much like rainbow-Wipe(), setting the color value of every LED on the strip based on the hue of the first LED. The actual animation happens in the outer loop, which increases the hue of the first LED every pass through the loop, shows the changes made and delays for the length of wait. Let's simplify the code a little by taking a look at just the outer loop and replace the inner loop with a stand-in.

```
for (long firstPixelHue = 0; firstPixelHue
< 65536; firstPixelHue += 256) {
```

```
// INNER FOR LOOP—set every LED on strip
to a different color on the spectrum
```

```
strip.show(); // show changes to colors
```

```
 delay(wait); // wait before moving on to
next step in animation
```

```
}
```

Instead of declaring int i = 0 as the index variable, this loop uses long firsPixelHue = 0. The condition is also much larger—the loop will run until the value of firstPixelHue < 65536.

Also, the increment is no longer i++. If the value of firstPixelHue was increased by only 1 every iteration of the loop, the loop would run 65,536 times, so we instead use firstPixelHue += 256. += is called the **compound addition operator**. It increases the value of the variable on the left by whatever value is on the right. In this case, since firstPixelHue is on the left and 256 is on the right, it increases the value of firstPixelHue by 256 after every iteration of the outer for loop.

You could change 256 to a different value, and it would still work fine, but it could affect how smooth the color transitions are. Dividing the maximum allowed value of firstPixelHue (65,536) by the increment (256) equals 256, so this loop will run 256 times before terminating.

The first part of the loop is the complete inner for loop. This loop will set the hue of the first pixel on the strip to whatever the current value of firstPixelHue is and then set the color values of all the other LEDs based on the hue of the first pixel, evenly distributing them around the color wheel.

At the end of the first for loop are strip.show() and delay(), which show whatever updates were made to the colors of the LEDs in the inner for loop and delay for a second, so the viewer's eye has time to process it.

The inner for loop works almost exactly like rainbowWipe()
but with one major difference.

```
for (int i = 0; i < strip.numPixels();
i++) {

// determine hue of current pixel being
set by loop

int hue = firstPixelHue + (i * (65536 /
strip.numPixels()));

// calculate RGB color value from hue and
perform gamma correction on it

uint32_t color = strip.gamma32(strip.
ColorHSV(hue));

//

strip.setPixelColor(i, color); // set color
of LED

}
```

This loop also sets the values of all the LEDs on the strip to
evenly distributed colors on the color wheel, but now the
value of each of those colors depends on the hue of the first
LED on the strip. Since this value will increment by 256 for
every new iteration of the outer for loop, this will essentially
shift every LED on the strip a little bit down the color wheel
every time. This creates the appearance of the rainbow flowing down the length of the strip.

7. COLOR WHEEL PARTICLES

We've spent most of our time so far using fairly linear "wipe" animations to explore the programming side of LED strips. But you can make LED strips light up in an infinite number of ways. In this final sketch, we're going to use the tools we've learned to make an entirely different kind of animation. We're also going to introduce a new function that you can use to introduce elements of randomness into your code.

Upload the following code to your Arduino and watch what happens.

```
LED_Strip_ColorWheelParticles | Arduino 1.8.13

LED_Strip_ColorWheelParticles
// LED Strip Programming 8

#include <Adafruit_NeoPixel.h>

const int STRIP_PIN = 6; // green wire of
const int LED_COUNT = 150; // number of LEDs on your strip (adjust if necessary)

long hue = 0; // current hue of LED to light
const int hueIncrement = 50; // change in hue for each new pixel

// declare new LED strip named "strip"
Adafruit_NeoPixel strip(LED_COUNT, STRIP_PIN, NEO_GRB + NEO_KHZ800);

void setup() {
  strip.begin(); // initialize strip
  strip.show(); // turn off all LEDs on strip
  strip.setBrightness(10); // set brightness level to 50 out of 255
}

void loop() {
  colorWheelParticles(100);
}

// randomly turns on LEDs using random colors
void colorWheelParticles(int wait) {
  int pixelToLight = random(strip.numPixels()); // randomly choose an LED "pixel" to light
  uint32_t color = strip.gamma32(strip.ColorHSV(hue)); // calculate RGB value from hue

  strip.setPixelColor(pixelToLight, color); // light a random pixel the new hue color
  strip.show(); // display changes made to LED settings
  delay(wait);

  hue += hueIncrement; // increment value of hue
}
```

34   Arduino Uno on /dev/cu.usbmodem145201

Random LEDs on your strip should begin to light up one after the other. After a little while, you may notice that each new

LED is a slightly different color from the last one that lit up and that the overall color of the entire strip is changing and becoming more chaotic.

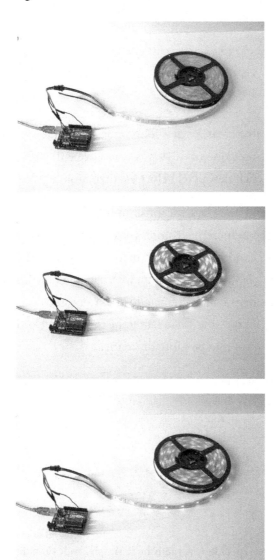

The first thing to notice about this sketch is that we've added two new lines to the section of code before setup().

```
long hue = 0; // current hue of LED to
light
```

```
const int hueIncrement = 50; // change
in hue for each new pixel
```

The first line creates a new long value called hue and assigns it a starting value of 0. This is where we will store the hue value of each new pixel before we turn it on.

The second line creates a constant int variable called hueIncrement. hueIncrement stores the difference in hue between each LED and the one placed before it, which in this case is 50. In other words, every time we turn on a new LED, we'll add the value of hueIncrement to hue. You could decrease this number if you want the effect to be more subtle or increase it if you want it to be more dramatic.

The loop() simply calls the animation we'll be focusing on this time.

```
void loop() {
```

```
colorWheelParticles(100);
```

```
}
```

colorWheelParticles() actually has a simpler code than most of the previous ones we've worked on.

```
// randomly turns on LEDs using random
colors
```

```
void colorWheelParticles(int wait) {
```

```
int pixelToLight = random(strip.numPix-
els()); // randomly choose an LED "pixel"
to light
```

```
uint32_t color = strip.gamma32(strip.
ColorHSV(hue)); // calculate RGB value
from hue
```

```
strip.setPixelColor(pixelToLight, color);
// light a random pixel the new hue color
```

```
strip.show(); // display changes made to
LED settings
```

```
delay(wait);
```

```
hue += hueIncrement; // increment value
of hue
```

```
}
```

There are no for loops to be dealt with here—every trip through the main loop() function only turns on one new LED. loop() calls exactly the same function with exactly the same argument every single time. And yet, a different LED turns on a different color every time. Why is this?

The main reason for this dramatic difference is this line right at the start of the function.

```
int pixelToLight = random(strip.
numPixels()); // randomly choose an LED
"pixel" to light
```

This creates a new int variable called pixelToLight and assigns it a random value using a function called random().

random() is, quite simply, a function that returns a random whole number. You can call it without passing any arguments to it, but it's usually most useful to call it using one of the following sets of parameters.

```
random(max)
```

```
random(min, max)
```

Here, max is the upper end of the range of numbers that random() is allowed to return. This is an *exclusive* maximum, meaning that the highest random number that could be generated with a given max is equal to max - 1. min, on the other hand, is the smallest number that random() is allowed to return and is *inclusive*. This means that if your minimum is 3, the function could actually return 3. If no min value is provided, the minimum will be set to 0 by default.

This means calling random(2, 10) will return a random number between 2 and 9, and calling random(5) will return a random number between 0 and 4.

In this sketch, we don't pass 2 or 10 or 5 as arguments—instead, we use strip.numPixels(). random(strip.numPixels()) will return a random number between 0 and one minus the number of LEDs on the LED strip. This is exactly the same set of numbers as the position values of all the LEDs on the strip since the first LED starts at 0.

If your LED strip has 150 LEDs, that means that pixelToLight could be assigned any value between 0 and 149. Essentially, this chooses a random pixel from the set of all pixels on the strip.

The code goes on to store an RGB color based on the current value of the variable hue, which is now defined above setup() rather than in the function itself.

```
uint32_t color = strip.gamma32(strip.
ColorHSV(hue)); // calculate RGB value
from hue
```

Then comes the moment of truth: This color value is assigned to the pixel randomly chosen by random().

```
strip.setPixelColor(pixelToLight, color);
// light a random pixel the new hue
color
```

The strip then updates and pauses for the length of the wait parameter...

```
strip.show(); // display changes made to
LED settings
```

```
delay(wait);
```

...and then increases the value of hue by the value of hueIncrement, making it so that the next time colorWheelParticles()

is run, the color the next randomly chosen LED is set to is slightly further around the color wheel than the last one.

```
hue += hueIncrement; // increment value
of hue
```

And that's it! The function runs again and again and again, filling up more and more LEDs with different colors.

Congratulations! You can now write some very complex code to make individually addressable LED strips light up in cool patterns. Now all that's left to do is learn how to use them to create your own works.

CHAPTER 11

LED STRIPS: ADVANCED HARDWARE

As the length of the LED strips used in your project grows, it becomes more and more difficult to meet their power and hardware needs. In this chapter, we're going to look at several more advanced ways to work with LED strips.

RUNNING MULTIPLE LED STRIPS SIMULTANEOUSLY

It's possible to run several LED strips at the same time using the NeoPixel library. However, because it takes time and processing power for the Arduino to handle the timing of several entirely separate strips simultaneously, you can only use three at the same time. If you try to add a fourth, the first three strips will run, but the fourth will remain off.

As an example, let's modify our original parameter_wipe() sketch to run on three separate LED strips at the same time, using three separate colors.

```
3_LED_Strip_Wipe
// LED wipe with 3 strips

#include <Adafruit_NeoPixel.h>

const int STRIP_1_PIN = 6; // pin connected to green wire of first LED strip
const int STRIP_2_PIN = 7; // pin connected to green wire of second LED strip
const int STRIP_3_PIN = 8; // pin connected to green wire of third LED strip

const int LED_COUNT = 150; // number of LEDs on each strip (adjust if necessary)

// create new LED strip objects
Adafruit_NeoPixel strip1(LED_COUNT, STRIP_1_PIN, NEO_GRB + NEO_KHZ800);
Adafruit_NeoPixel strip2(LED_COUNT, STRIP_2_PIN, NEO_GRB + NEO_KHZ800);
Adafruit_NeoPixel strip3(LED_COUNT, STRIP_3_PIN, NEO_GRB + NEO_KHZ800);

void setup() {
  // initialze strips
  strip1.begin();
  strip2.begin();
  strip3.begin();

  // turn off all LEDs on strips
  strip1.show();
  strip2.show();
  strip3.show();

  // set brightness level of strips to 50 out of 255
  strip1.setBrightness(50);
  strip2.setBrightness(50);
  strip3.setBrightness(50);
}

void loop() {
  wipe();
}
```

Arduino Uno on /dev/cu.usbmodem145201

The only fundamental difference between this sketch and the original one is that it declares three separate Adafruit_NeoPixel objects with three different names that are connected to three different pins. Now, instead of calling a method such as setPixelColor() by simply calling strip.setPixelColor(), you must call the specific Adafruit_Neopixel object connected to the LED strip you want to control, such as strip1.setPixelColor() or strip2.setPixelColor().

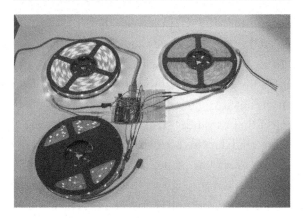

PROTECTING YOUR LEDS AND MAXIMIZING SIGNAL TRANSMISSION

A large part of electrical engineering has to do with **signal processing**, or the methods by which electrically transmitted information is altered during transmission. In many cases, we want signals to change when they go through a certain system—for example, the electrical signal produced by an electric guitar is naturally very weak and very simple. In order to make that signal useful, we have to modify it by putting it through guitar pedals that distort the sound in interesting ways and then put the modified signal into an amplifier that makes it loud enough to be heard from far away.

In a lot of cases, though, the most important thing is to minimize change to the electrical signal. That's the case with LED strips: Your Arduino is capable of outputting a near-perfect signal for the LEDs to read. The world, however, is not perfect, and several factors can affect the quality and accuracy of this signal.

1. The length of the wire between the Arduino and each LED. All wiring has some small amount of resistance in it. In most cases we deal with at the scale of the projects in this book, this resistance is so little that it doesn't matter, but if you're connecting an Arduino to a large project that uses LED strips and you need to use a long wire to send data to the strip, that small amount of resistance in every few inches of wire can add up and ultimately weaken the signal. This is especially important because the connections between LEDs on the strip also contain a very small amount of resistance, meaning the

signal will weaken even more the farther down the strip each LED is.

2. The presence of random electrical noise in the Arduino and in other wires and electronics near it. The movement of electrons influences the movement of other electrons nearby, which can create electrical noise that can interfere with some weaker signals. If there's enough electrical noise affecting the signal being sent to your LED strip, LEDs can sometimes be set to the wrong color, or the wrong LEDs could be selected, or both.

The recommended way to solve this issue is to add a little bit of extra hardware to the basic LED strip setup. You only need two components: a 470Ω resistor and a 1000μF capacitor.

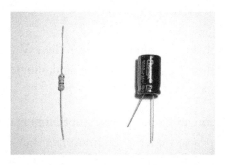

Capacitors are electronic components that act kind of like really small rechargeable batteries. When powered, they store a little bit of electrical charge, and when unpowered, they slowly release it. The amount of charge they can hold depends on the voltage applied and is measured in units called **farads**. One farad, as it happens, is a very large amount of charge, so most capacitors store much, much smaller amounts. A more common measurement is the **microfarad**, or **μF**. One microfarad is equal to 10^{-6} farads, or one one-millionth of a farad.

Capacitors are often used to filter out unwanted noise from circuits and to protect against sudden power surges. Adding additional resistance to the signal pin also lowers the probability that a sudden power surge could damage the first LED on the strip.

To protect your LEDs from power surges and clarify the signal, add a capacitor and a 470Ω resistor to the basic LED strip connection setup like so:

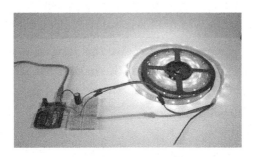

The capacitor should connect between the +5V wire and the GND wire. The resistor, on the other hand, should be in series with the signal wire.

There are many different types of capacitors made of many different types of materials. Sometimes they can behave a little differently because of this. The capacitors used to protect LED strips are usually a rather common type called **electrolytic capacitors**. This is only worthy of note because, unlike some kinds of capacitors, electrolytic capacitors are polar, so putting them in backward can sometimes damage them.

Electrolytic capacitors generally have a white strip on the side of one of the capacitor's two leads. The lead on the same side as this strip is typically the negative lead—make sure this is the one you connect to GND, and make sure the non-negative lead is the one connected to +5V.

POWERING MANY LEDS

As the size and scale of your projects increases, you may find that connecting LED strips directly to an Arduino UNO is insufficient for your needs, whether because the UNO can't output enough power for hundreds of LEDs or because it can't run as many separate LED strips as you need it to. This section provides a few suggestions for how to overcome these issues.

UPGRADING YOUR ARDUINO

So far, we've exclusively used an Arduino UNO board for the projects in this book. The UNO is a well-made, highly capable board, but for more complex projects that use many inputs and outputs, it can sometimes be helpful to upgrade.

One option I recommend is the Arduino MEGA 2560. The Mega works basically identically to the UNO and is programmed exactly the same way but has many more pins and is built using a more powerful microcontroller that can transmit and receive information on more different channels at the same time.

For projects that involve large numbers of LED strips, the Mega is often a better choice than the UNO because it can handle the more intensive memory and connectivity requirements of such projects. It's a very useful tool for your toolbox.

CALCULATING YOUR POWER NEEDS

It's easy to forget when using LED strips that they're really not more than large numbers of individual LEDs strung together. Each of those LEDs requires a small, manageable amount of current in order to run. However, when the total number of LEDs reaches the hundreds or thousands, that manageable amount of current can quickly become too large for an Arduino to provide.

The I/O pins on an Arduino UNO board have a maximum current output of about 20 milliamps, which is a relatively small amount. In fact, a single AdaFruit Neopixel LED drawing maximum power uses 60 milliamps of current, which is three times that.

Of course, the actual power draw will likely be less than this, depending on the exact nature of your project. If you don't turn your LEDs on to full brightness, they'll draw considerably less power. Setting the LEDs to some colors will also draw more power than others. A more realistic estimate is that each LED running at full strength will use around 20 milliamps. This will necessarily be less when the Arduino is powering your LED strips directly, meaning that you'll need to power them externally to get the highest performance you can out of them.

To approximate your current needs, multiply the number of LEDs your project uses by 20 milliamps (0.02 amps). For example, if your project uses 500 LEDs, then you would need to supply your LED strips with:

500 x 0.02 amps = 10 amps

Ten amps of current. This is actually a very large amount. Ten amps of current delivered directly to an Arduino would fry it. So, in order to power this many LEDs while still being able to control them with an Arduino, we're going to have to get a little creative.

USING A DC POWER SUPPLY

So far, we've only ever supplied power to the Arduino by connecting it to the computer using the USB cable. However, once code has been uploaded, Arduinos don't need to be connected to the computer to operate. Instead, you can connect it to a battery or power supply.

For projects that require large numbers of LEDs, I recommend finding a DC power supply like the one below.

These can connect directly to the Arduino's circular black DC power jack and will provide a steady power source for the Arduino and all the components attached to it. Make sure to find one that's rated to supply between 7-12 volts, as that's the range of voltages that the Arduino is designed to be supplied with. The current rating is slightly less important, but ideally, you'll want to use a power supply that can provide more than enough amps of current to run all of your LEDs.

USING AN EXTERNAL VOLTAGE DIVIDER

One method of powering LED strips that I often use involves using an integrated circuit like the one below.

This is called a **voltage divider**. Voltage dividers are a type of integrated circuit that takes higher voltages as input and outputs a steady lower voltage, burning off the rest of the energy as heat.

This allows us to power the Arduino using a 7-12V DC power supply, then take a direct line from that higher voltage and drop it down to 5V so it can be used to power LED strips separately. The advantage to this method is that by creating an alternate path from the power supply to the LEDs, you can access the full DC current supply provided by the power supply instead of having to work with the smaller current provided by the Arduino.

The most common 5V voltage divider is the L7805, which is the same as the one pictured above. In order to use the L7805 safely and reliably, you have to add two additional capacitors. One of them is a 0.33µF (microfarad) tantalum capacitor like the one pictured below. The other is a 0.1µF ceramic capacitor.

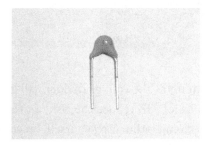

To use the voltage divider to supply power to your LED strips, connect the left lead to the VIN pin on your Arduino, connect the center pin to the ground, and connect the right pin to the +5V wire on the LED strip. (Note: these directions are only correct if you orient the voltage divider as it is in the photo above.)

Once those main connections are in place, connect the 0.33µF tantalum capacitor between the input and ground, and connect the 0.1µF ceramic capacitor between output and ground. These will help to stabilize the input signal and protect the circuit.

The image below shows the voltage divider setup on a breadboard. For this to work (and for there to be any point in going through the effort of setting it up at all), you must connect the Arduino to a 7-12 volt DC power supply. The voltage divider will then lower the voltage to 5V and deliver it directly to the LED strip at a higher current than you could get from the Arduino.

One important note: The voltage divider will likely get very hot as it does its job. To reduce the risk of overheating and damaging the circuit or burning yourself, I recommend purchasing some small **heat sinks** like the ones pictured below, pieces of metal that are shaped in a way that maximizes their surface area so as to wick away heat faster.

You can then attach one to the metal plate on the voltage divider, which is itself a heat sink, to cool it down faster. If it's still too hot, consider attaching additional heat sinks to other surfaces on the voltage divider.

THE FASTLED LIBRARY

In this book, we use the Adafruit NeoPixel library to run LED strips. This is a simple, standard library that runs well on an Arduino UNO and will give a beginner pretty much anything they need.

However, many experienced Arduino users will tell you that the NeoPixel library is bloated, inefficient, and limited in its capabilities. They are correct. Another option is the FastLED library. The FastLED library is much more efficient and uses far less storage space on your Arduino per LED used, especially when it comes to running much larger and more complex LED displays with high frame rates. It's not even really any harder to use—the methods in the library are a little different, but fundamentally it works the same way.

The only real downside to the FastLED library is that the base library size is large enough that an Arduino UNO can struggle to contain it, which is why it isn't used in this book. The memory usage per LED is far smaller than for the NeoPixel Library, but that doesn't really matter if the basic library is too big for the Arduino.

CHAPTER 12

ARDUINO + PROCESSING

Tools needed:

- Laptop computer (1)
- USB A to B cable (1)

Parts needed:

- Arduino UNO (1)

At some point, you may want to use an Arduino to control graphics on a computer screen, monitor, or projector. If this day ever comes, you may want to consider using **Processing**, a programming language designed to make programming complex computer graphics as easy as possible.[5]

---

5   Processing Foundation, Processing 3 Logo, 2015.

As it happens, Processing and Arduino have a long history. Arduino, as it happens, is partially based on Processing. They both use C++ syntax and resemble each other in every significant way. This makes it very easy for them to work together.

Using the serial commands you've already learned, it's possible to send data between the Arduino and Processing one byte at a time. This allows the Arduino to collect sensory data and use it to control graphics made using Processing and for Processing to collect data from the computer and use it to control the Arduino.

In this chapter, we're going to take a look at how to establish a data link between an Arduino and Processing. We aren't going to spend too much time exploring how to use Processing to create graphics—this is an Arduino book, and the exploration of Processing deserves its own book.

ESTABLISHING A CONNECTION

Before we can connect Arduino and Processing, we need to make sure they're both communicating via the correct serial port. Every USB or Bluetooth device connected to your computer is assigned a different serial port to communicate through, so it's a good idea to go through this process to make sure you're using the right port every time you connect your Arduino to the computer with the intention of having it communicate with Processing.

1. Download and install Processing from processing.org.

2. Open the application. A window that looks like this should appear.

Does this look familiar to you? It should—the Arduino IDE is directly modeled on the Processing IDE.

1. Type the following code into Processing and save it as "Processing_Connection_Test."

1. Connect your Arduino UNO to your computer via USB just like you normally would. Upload the following code.

```
Arduino_Connection_Test | Arduino 1.8.13

Arduino_Connection_Test
// Connection Test

const int LED_PIN = 13;

void setup() {
  Serial.begin(9600);
  pinMode(LED_PIN, OUTPUT);
}

void loop() {
  if (Serial.available()) { // if data is present in the serial buffer
    if (Serial.read() == 'o') {
      digitalWrite(LED_PIN, HIGH);
      delay(500);
      digitalWrite(LED_PIN, LOW);
    }
  }
}

18                              Arduino Uno on /dev/cu.usbmodem145201
```

1. Now press the "play" button in the Processing window. A tiny grey window like the one shown below should appear.

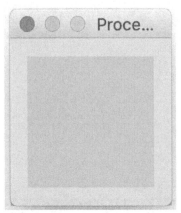

1. We're going to ignore this window for now. A list like the one below should also appear in the console.

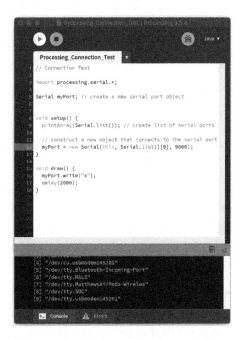

1. This is a list of all the available serial ports that Processing can communicate with. Only one of them connects to your Arduino, and we need to figure out which one that is.

2. To find out what the correct serial port is, go back to the Arduino IDE and open the serial monitor. The correct port is named at the top of the window.

In this case, the correct port is called "/dev/cu.usbmo-dem145201." This was port number 9 in the list shown in the Processing console, so port 9 is the one we want. The port your Arduino is connected to will likely be a different number on the list—compare the port name from this window to the list printed in the console in your Processing IDE and find the correct port number for your computer.

1. Go back to the Processing IDE and take a look at this line of code.

```
myPort = new Serial(this, Serial.list()[7],
9600);
```

2. This line is how Processing connects to a given serial port. Right now, the code is connecting to port number 7. Change the number 7 in this line to whatever port number your Arduino is connected to.

3. Press "run" on the Processing IDE one more time, taking note of how the Arduino's onboard LED is behaving before you press the button. It should be completely off. After you press "run," the Arduino should begin to blink about once every second.

UNDERSTANDING THE PROCESSING CODE

This book is about Arduino, so we won't go into every single nitty-gritty detail about how the Processing code in this project works. We will, however, be taking a general look at the code and comparing it to how an Arduino sketch would function so you can get a better idea of what's happening with the data transfer here.

The first line is a little different than what you might see in an Arduino sketch.

```
import processing.serial.*;
```

Unlike in an Arduino sketch, if you want to use serial communication with Processing, you have to import a library called processing.serial and create a Serial object to handle the communication, much as you might have to do to communicate with an LED strip on Arduino. This line functions just like an Arduino import statement but imports a library for Processing instead.

```
Serial myPort; // create a new serial port
object
```

This line creates a Serial object using the library imported above that Processing can use to communicate via the serial ports.

```
void setup() {

printArray(Serial.list()); // create list
of serial ports

// construct a new object that connects
to the serial port

myPort = new Serial(this, Serial.list()[7],
9600);

}
```

Just like in any Arduino sketch, here we have a setup() function to establish any initial settings or bits of code before moving on to the rest of the sketch. There are two functioning lines of code here. Here's the first:

```
printArray(Serial.list()); // create list
of serial ports
```

printArray() is a function in Processing used to quickly print a numbered array of data to the terminal on the bottom of the IDE window. Serial.list() is a method of the Serial class in Processing that outputs an array containing every serial port currently open on your computer. Combining the two of these is what gives us the list of available serial ports used to determine the port number we need to access.

The next line is:

```
myPort = new Serial(this, Serial.list()[7],
9600);
```

This line is a constructor for the myPort object. We won't explore this in too much detail, but note that the number in the second argument's square brackets should be whatever port number you're trying to communicate with (i.e., the one that the Arduino is connected to), and that the third parameter should be the same baud rate as the Arduino is communicating at—in most cases, 9600 baud.

Now we come across something that at first glance seems new but is essentially just a reskin of the Arduino syntax.

```
void draw() {
```

```
myPort.write("a");
```

```
delay(2000);
```

```
}
```

Because Processing is a language designed to make it very easy to create graphics, the function we would call loop() in Arduino programming is called draw() in Processing—in every other way, they are identical. This draw() function will loop forever, just as loop() would.

Because we've created a Serial object called myPort that connects to the same serial port as an Arduino, we can now use most of the Serial methods we're used to using in Arduino using that object. Hence:

```
myPort.write("a");
```

This writes the letter "a" to the serial port for the Arduino to read.

Last but not least, we add a delay() function to keep from overflowing the Arduino's limited serial buffer.

```
delay(2000);
```

And that wraps up the Processing sketch! Now let's take a look at the Arduino half of things—the receiving end.

UNDERSTANDING THE ARDUINO CODE

There isn't a whole lot to understand with this Arduino code—it's all things we've used before.

The first part of the code creates a variable to store the onboard LED pin number in, then runs a setup() function to start serial communication and initialize the LED pin as an output.

```
const int LED _ PIN = 13;

void setup() {

Serial.begin(9600);

pinMode(LED _ PIN, OUTPUT);

}
```

And all the loop() does is check to see if any serial data has been received—if it has, and if that serial data is the letter "a," it blinks the light on for half a second before turning it off again.

```
void loop() {

if (Serial.available()) { // if data is present in the serial buffer

if (Serial.read() == 'a') {

digitalWrite(LED _ PIN, HIGH);

delay(500);

digitalWrite(LED _ PIN, LOW);

}
```

```
}
```

```
}
```

Simple stuff.

So, in short, what happens here is that the Arduino turns on, connects to the serial port associated with the USB port it's connected to, and waits to receive an "a" via that serial port. Processing connects to the same serial port and outputs an "a" every 2 seconds. Thus, every two seconds, the Arduino receives an "a" and blinks the onboard LED in response.

Once you've confirmed that the Arduino and Processing are communicating using the same serial port, you can move on to bigger and better things. In the next project, we're going to reverse the direction of communication and send data from the Arduino to Processing, which can then generate computer graphics based on this information.

CHANGE BACKGROUND COLOR

Run the following Arduino sketch, and then run the following Processing sketch (in that order). Make sure your Processing sketch is using the correct serial port number!

```
Arduino_Change_Background | Arduino 1.8.13

Arduino_Change_Background
// Change Background Color

void setup() {
  Serial.begin(9600);
}

void loop() {
  Serial.println('r');
  delay(1000);
  Serial.println('g');
  delay(1000);
  Serial.println('b');
  delay(1000);
}
```
```
13                          Arduino Uno on /dev/cu.usbmodem145201
```

```
Processing_Change_Background | Processing 3.5.4

                                                        Java ▾

Processing_Change_Background   ▾

1    // Change Background Color
2
3    import processing.serial.*;
4
5    Serial myPort; // create a new serial port object
6
7    int data; // stores data recieved from Arduino
8
9    void setup() {
10     // construct a new object that connects to the serial port
11     myPort = new Serial(this, Serial.list()[7], 9600);
12   }
13
14   void draw() {
15     if (myPort.available() > 0) {
16       data = myPort.read(); // read data from Arduino
17
18       if (data == 'r') {
19         background(255, 0, 0); // change background color
20       } if (data == 'g') {
21         background(0, 255, 0);
22       } if (data == 'b') {
23         background(0, 0, 255);
24       }
25     }
26   }
```

```
>_ Console     ⚠ Errors
```

If everything is running properly, the little graphical window in Processing should open up and cycle between three colors: red, green, and blue.

UNDERSTANDING THE ARDUINO CODE

As in the last project, there isn't much new to understand about this Arduino code.

First, we begin serial communication in setup().

```
void setup() {

Serial.begin(9600);

}
```

Then in the loop(), the Arduino outputs 'r,' 'g,' and 'b,' characters in a cycle with one-second delays in between them.

```
void loop() {

Serial.println('r');

delay(1000);

Serial.println('g');

delay(1000);

Serial.println('b');

delay(1000);

}
```

This time, the Arduino is serving as the output device, and now we're working with three different output signals—the characters 'r,' 'g,' and 'b.' Now, we need to receive and interpret this data in Processing.

UNDERSTANDING THE PROCESSING SKETCH

The Processing sketch begins much the same way as last time, with the addition of the declaration of a variable called data that will be used to store received serial data.

```
import processing.serial.*;

Serial myPort; // create a new serial port
object

int data; // stores data recieved from
Arduino
```

setup() is exactly the same as last time, constructing the myPort Serial object and connecting it to the appropriate port number.

```
void setup() {

// construct a new object that connects
to the serial port

myPort = new Serial(this, Serial.list()[7],
9600);

}
```

If Processing doesn't seem to be receiving serial data, run the previous connection test sketches again and make sure that Processing is communicating with the same serial port the Arduino is attached to.

The draw() function, however, now looks a lot like the Arduino's loop() function did when it was receiving data.

```
void draw() {

if (myPort.available() > 0) {

data = myPort.read(); // read data from Arduino

if (data == 'r') {

background(255, 0, 0); // change background color

} if (data == 'g') {

background(0, 255, 0);

} if (data == 'b') {

background(0, 0, 255);

}

}

}
```

draw() now checks to see if data is present in the serial port attached to myPort for every iteration of this loop of code. If there is data present, it stores the information in the data variable. It then compares the value of the data stored in that variable to the characters 'r,' 'g,' and 'b.' If it matches one of them, the background color is set to the corresponding RGB color using a function called background(), which takes red, green, and blue values from 0-255 as parameters.

Because the Arduino cycles through which of the three characters it writes to the serial port, the Processing sketch will always receive the three characters in the same order. It then interprets this data and updates the graphics in its onscreen window appropriately.

GLOSSARY

- **#include**—A syntactical term used in C++ and Arduino programming to "include" libraries, i.e., add their functionality to a sketch.

- **Alternating current (AC)**—A type of electrical circuit where the direction of current changes many times per second.

- **Analog communication**—The transfer of information by using a large spectrum of possible values within a range.

- **Arduino**—A brand of microcontroller platform that makes it very easy to work with electronics. Many different models of Arduino boards are sold.

- **Arduino UNO**—The most popular model of Arduino board.

- **Arguments**—The actual values that a function is given when it is called. Related to parameters.

- **Binary code**—The computer language made up of ones and zeroes you've probably seen in the movies.

- **Block**—A portion of code bounded by "curly braces" (the '{' and '}' characters, respectively) that functions as a complete unit.

- **Breadboards**—Allows the user to quickly, easily, and temporarily connect electronic components together to test circuits. Breadboarding is a midway point between just twisting wires together and attaching components together permanently. Rather than using individual pieces of wire to connect everything, it's often far easier to just hook up components to a breadboard.

- **Brightness**—How dark or bright a color is. If you took a black-and-white image of a bright color, it would appear closer to white, while a dark color might look more like black.

- **Button**—A type of electrical switch that allows or prohibits electricity from flowing through it depending on whether it is pressed.

- **Camel case**—A naming convention in programming where the first letter of a name is lowercase and the first letter of every other word in the name is capitalized, such as in newAwesomeVariable. It gets its name because the capital letters kind of look like a camel's hump.

- **Capacitors**—Electronic components that act kind of like really small rechargeable batteries. When powered, they store a little bit of electrical charge, and when unpowered, they slowly release it. The amount of charge they can hold depends on the voltage applied and is measured in units called farads.

- **char**—A data type similar to the String type, except that instead of storing a string of text, it can only store a single character, such as a letter or number.

- **Comparison operator**—A little code "symbol" that tells the Arduino how two different numbers relate to each other.

- **const**—A variable qualifier that indicates to the compiler that a variable's value will remain constant for the entire duration of the program so that it can reduce memory usage.

- **Digital** communication is the transfer of information by using one of two possible different values.

- **Direct current (DC)**—The type of electrical circuit most often used in small devices and in conjunction with Arduino. A direct-current circuit is any circuit where the direction of current flow remains constant.

- **Distance sensors**—Electronic devices that can tell an Arduino how far away an object is. They're used quite frequently in robotics to help robots avoid obstacles, but they have also found a home in art, where they're commonly used to sense where a viewer is in relation to the art piece.

- **Electrolytic capacitors**—A common type of capacitor. Unlike some kinds of capacitors, electrolytic capacitors are polar, so putting them in backward can sometimes damage them. Electrolytic capacitors generally have a white strip on the side of one of the capacitor's two leads. The lead on the same side as this strip is typically the negative lead—make sure this is the one you connect to GND and make sure the non-negative lead is the one connected to +5V.

- **Else statement**—An extension of an if statement which executes a different block of code if the condition in the if statement is *not* true. Here's the basic format of an if statement:

- **Farad**—The standard unit of capacitance.

- **Female header pins**—Small connectors that are used to attach electronic circuitry to the Arduino by allowing wires to plug directly into them. Each of these pins on the Arduino UNO has a number to identify it. Often abbreviated to simply "pins."

- **For loops**—One of the three types of loops you can write in C++. It runs a block of code a specific, predetermined number of times.

- **Function**—A piece of code that performs a specific function and sometimes returns a value.

- **Functional programming**—A method of programming which emphasizes the use of functions to work with data.

- **Gamma correction**—The process of altering colors so that they will be perceived correctly by the human eye, which is more sensitive to some wavelengths of colors than others.

- **Ground**—The part of a circuit where the electric potential is 0 volts. It creates what is known as a "potential difference" that causes electricity to flow from parts of the circuit with higher voltages to ground.

- **Hardware**—All the physical parts of your circuit that connect to each other.

- **Heat sinks**–Pieces of metal shaped in a way that maximizes their surface area so as to wick away heat faster.

- **Hue**—The position of a color on the color spectrum. Determines whether a color is one of the primary colors or somewhere in between.

- **If statement**—A construct in a programming language that only executes a specified block of code if a certain condition is true.

- **Individually addressable LED strip**—An LED strip that can set the color of each LED on the strip independently. By adding a tiny silicon chip alongside every RGB LED in an LED strip, it becomes possible for each individual LED in an individually addressable LED strip to remember what color it's supposed to be. This means that a microcontroller such as an Arduino can *individually address* each LED on the strip and tell each one to be a different color at a different point in time.

- **Infrared distance sensors**—A type of distance sensor that calculates the distance between the sensor and an obstacle by sending out a pulse of infrared (IR) light. The light then bounces off the surface of the obstacle and returns to the sensor. The sensor measures the angle at which the IR light returns to approximate the distance from which it bounced back. IR distance sensors tend to be somewhat imprecise, so they're most useful for measuring the presence or absence of an obstacle rather than obtaining highly accurate distance calculations. Also known as IR distance sensors.

- **int**—A variable type that can store integers, AKA whole numbers.

- **Japanese Solderless Terminal (JST)**—A small snap connector used to allow wires to be easily connected and disconnected. Sometimes found on infrared distance sensors.

- **Lead**—A small piece of wire that sticks out of an electrical component so that it can be connected to something else. Pronounced "leeds."

- **LED strips**—Very long, thin, and flexible circuit boards with evenly spaced LEDs mounted on them.

- **LEDs**—Small electrical components that emit light. They're also much more energy-efficient than lightbulbs and produce a lot more light from a given amount of energy. Make sure not to push current through them in the wrong direction, or they could break.

- **long**—A variable type that can store very large integers.

- **Loop**—A programming structure that encloses a block of code and runs it multiple times, just like how the loop() function runs its contents over and over again until the Arduino is turned off.

- **Multi-line comment**—A comment in a piece of code that can stretch across multiple lines. It opens with /* and closes with */.

- **Normally Closed (NC)**—A button that electricity can pass through unless it is being pressed.

- **Normally Open (NO)**—A button that electricity cannot pass through unless it is being pressed.

- **Object**—A little bundle of code that can use its own functions (known as "methods") and store data that relates to the object.

- **Object oriented programming**—A method of writing code that focuses on organizing data into self-contained "objects."

- **Onboard LED**—An LED light that is hard-wired to pin 13 on the Arduino. Labeled with an L on the surface of the Arduino board.

- **Parameters**—The values that a function needs in order to run.

- **Processing**—A programming language designed to make programming complex computer graphics as easy as possible.

- **Pulse-width-modulation (PWM)**—A method that digital systems such as Arduinos can use to simulate analog signals. On an Arduino, when an "analog" output command is sent to a pin that can use PWM, the pin will output a digital HIGH for a certain length of time and then output a digital LOW for a certain amount of time, modulating this length based on the analog value needed to be transmitted. The effect this has is to average out the HIGH and LOW signals to effectively become something in between.

- **Resistors**—Electrical components that add specific amounts of resistance to circuits, allowing the user to control exactly how much current is flowing through the circuit or a part of the circuit. Resistors come in many different resistance values (measured in ohms), which are indicated by their pattern of colored stripes.

- **return**—A command used inside a function to return a value or the value of a variable. If your function has a type other than void, it *must* have a return command in the function definition or you'll get an error.

- **Return**—When a function returns a value, it essentially sets itself equal to that value. That value can then be assigned to a variable or compared to other things, just like any other value.

- **Return type**—The type of value a function will return, whether it be int, char, String, or something else.

- **RGB LEDs**—LEDs that can be set to glow in any RGB color.

- **RPM**—Rotations per minute. A unit of rotational speed.

- **Saturation**—How intense a color is. Bright apple-red would be a high saturation color, whereas a pastel pink would be lower saturation.

- **Semicolon**—something you should never, ever forget.

- **Serial communication**—Morse code for computers. By sending complex patterns of electric pulses through wires, you can transmit information from one place to another.

- **Serial monitor**—A window on the Arduino IDE that allows you to send and receive messages from the Arduino while it's running. Not only is this invaluable for

How to Create Stunning Multimedia Art with Electronics

debugging complex code, it also opens up the possibility of using a computer to control an Arduino and vice versa. This means that you could connect a light display to an Arduino and use your computer to control it in real-time or send input data collected by the Arduino back to the computer to control a digital display.

- **Servo motors**—A special type of motor that will turn to any specific position you tell them to rotate to. Highly useful for any project that requires things to move with a small but highly precise range of motion.

- **Signal processing**—The methods by which electrically transmitted information is altered during transmission.

- **Single-line comment**—A comment in a piece of code that begins with // and ends at the end of the line. Allows the coder to leave notes to themselves and others, label sections of code, and indicate the function of various sections of code.

- **Sketch**—The Arduino term for the code that you upload to an Arduino in order to make it behave how you want it to.

- **Software**—The intangible code instructions that we upload to the hardware so it knows what to do.

- **Stranded wires**—An alternative to solid-core wires. Instead of being one solid piece of copper coated in insulation, these wires are actually bundles of many different, smaller wires.

- **String**—A data type that holds "strings" of text. Strings must always be enclosed in double quotes.

- **Torque**—Rotational force. A motor's torque determines how much weight it can rotate.

- **uint32_t**—A data type that is essentially a special version of an integer. It's not used very commonly in Arduino programming but is typically the go-to data type for storing color values for use with LED strips. The "u" stands for "unsigned," meaning "doesn't have a positive or negative value." The "32_t" indicates that this kind of integer is made to store exactly 32 bits of data—no more, no less.

- **Ultrasonic distance sensors**—A type of distance sensor that calculates the distance between the sensor and an obstacle by sending out a pulse of extremely high-pitched ultrasonic sound (so high-pitched, in fact, that humans can't hear it). The sound then bounces off the surface of the obstacle and returns to the sensor. The sensor measures the time elapsed between transmitting the pulse and the pulse returning to the sensor. Because sound travels at an approximately constant speed on earth, the elapsed time can then be used to calculate the distance between the obstacle and the sensor. Programming ultrasonic distance sensors are a little bit more complicated because the timing has to be measured very precisely, but the advantage is that they tend to be more accurate and have a longer range.

- **Variable**—A construct in a programming language that can store values for later use.

- **Variable declaration**—The process of initializing a new variable in a program.

- **Variable qualifier**—A programming keyword that modifies the behavior of the variable declared after it.

- **Variable type**—The type of information that can be stored in a variable.

- **Voltage divider**—A type of integrated circuit that takes higher voltages as input and outputs a steady lower voltage, burning off the rest of the energy as heat.

- **Wires**—What humans use to control the flow of electricity. When electricity moves through a wire, it must follow the path of the wire. Wires do to electricity what pipes do to water: They funnel it to specific locations.

ACKNOWLEDGMENTS

———

This book would not exist without the support of many people.

First, all of the contributors to the *Arduino for Artists* Indie-GoGo campaign: Chuck and Katie McClain, Marvin and Patricia McClain, Caitlin Welsh, Diego Porqueras, Noah Chaoli, Brian Skyers, Marly Gonzalez, Queenie Taylor, Stephanie, James, and Ethan Irey, Emmanuel Csiki, Stephen Rice, Jon Gowling, Benjamin Straus, Jorge Bachmann, Chun Bong Fung, Don and Alice Gatz, Laurie Walz, Ethan Block, Bob and Chris McClain, Katherine McClain, Joshua Miller, Wesley Heiss, Joze Reza, Logan LaClair, Jessica and Justin Hirigoyen, Brian Walsh, Thomas Shoff, Travis Martinez, Eric Koester, Mahshid Hager, Joan McClain, Camille Liscinsky, Adam Belling, Crispin Harris, Laurie Lew, Cadence Tam, Tri Nguyen, Joshua Home Edwards, Mikayla Spott, Em Thampoe, Mary Rose McClain, Jessica Vogel, Josh Kramer, Shayna Sternin, Laurie Walz, Jake Kaplow, Nathan Clum, and Nate Odenkirk.

Second, I'd like to thank the teams at the Book Creators Program and New Degree Press, including Professor Eric Koester, Brian Bies, Natalie Lucas, and Jason Chinchen.

Finally, I'd like to thank the many other people who have supported me along the long, tumultuous journey that led to this book's existence, such as my parents, who supported and funded my fascination with tinkering around with electronics in my childhood; my grandfather Marvin McClain, who bought me my first Arduino UNO without fully understanding what it was; my friend Josh Kramer, who asked me to start a robotics club with him in tenth grade; all the members of Oakwood Robotics who put up with my type-A personality and let me teach them Arduino; Phu Tranchi, for supporting our little robotics club for years and for suggesting that I make an Arduino robotics curriculum for my senior project, which would one day become this book; Ben McIntosh, for being my teacher, mentor, boss, and friend through my adolescence and for giving me my first big break as a STEAM educator; my maker mentor Diego Porqueras, who taught me everything I know about 3D printers and LED strips; my friend Molly Benning, for being my rock during the process of writing this book; and Rich, Laura, and Luke Benning, who let me live in their house during the summer of 2020 while I wrote this book.

Without the guidance and support of these many dozens of people, this book would never have been written. I thank you all deeply.

APPENDIX

INTRODUCTION

Mischer'Traxler Studios. *Plural.* 2019. Motors, elastic string, and
electronics. Futurium, Berlin. https://mischertraxler.com/
projects/plural-and-spannungsfeld/

INFRARED DISTANCE SENSORS

Kotian, Juraj. *Reflection of the Age.* 2015. Aluminum,
polystyrene, ultrasonic range finder, Arduino MEGA,
electrical wires. https://www.behance.net/gallery/27308485/
Reflection-of-the-Age-Mammon?isao=1

PLAYING WITH LED STRIPS

Lowry, Will and Melpomene Katakalos. *Spring Awakening.* 2019.
Wood and LED light strips. Diamond Theater, Zoellner Arts
Center, Lehigh University, Bethlehem, Pennsylvania.

ARDUINO + PROCESSING

Processing Foundation. Processing 3 Logo. 2015.

Made in the USA
Coppell, TX
28 September 2021

63168263R00157